MW00668601

<u>Legal Notice</u>

For information on bulk purchases and licensing agreements, please email

support@SATPrepGet800.com

ISBN-13: 978-1-951619-00-8

This is the Solution Guide to the book
"Pure Mathematics for Pre-Beginners."

Also Available from Dr. Steve Warner

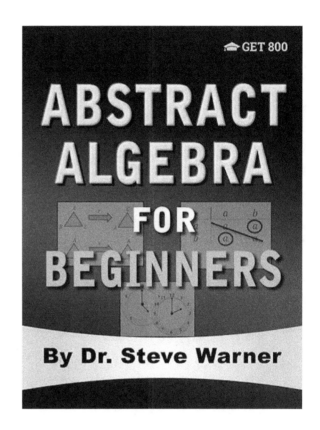

CONNECT WITH DR. STEVE WARNER

www.facebook.com/SATPrepGet800

www.youtube.com/TheSATMathPrep

www.twitter.com/SATPrepGet800

www.linkedin.com/in/DrSteveWarner

www.pinterest.com/SATPrepGet800

Also Available from Dr. Steve Warner

CONNECT WITH DR. STEVE WARNER

www.facebook.com/SATPrepGet800

www.youtube.com/TheSATMathPrep

www.twitter.com/SATPrepGet800

www.linkedin.com/in/DrSteveWarner

www.pinterest.com/SATPrepGet800

Pure Mathematics for Pre-Beginners

Solution Guide

Dr. Steve Warner

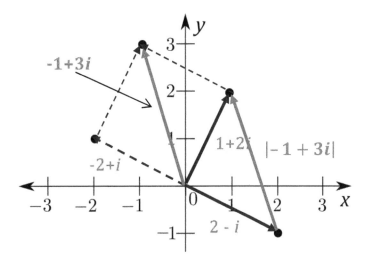

Table of Contents

Problem Set 1

LEVEL 1

Determine whether each of the following sentences is an atomic statement, a compound statement, or not a statement at all:

1. Grace is not going shopping tomorrow.

This is a **compound statement**. It has the form $\neg p$, where p is the statement "Grace is going shopping tomorrow."

2. Where did I go wrong?

This is **not a statement**. It is a question.

3. Stay out of my way today.

This is **not a statement**. It is a command.

4. $x > 26$.

This is **not a statement**. It has an unknown variable.

5. I visited the law firm of Cooper and Smith.

This is an **atomic statement**. Even though the word "and" appears in the statement, here it is part of the name of the law firm. It is not being used as a connective.

6. If there is an elephant in the room, then we need to talk.

This is a **compound statement**. It has the form $p \rightarrow q$, where p is the statement "There is an elephant in the room," and q is the statement "We need to talk."

7. $2 < -7$ or $15 > 100$.

This is a **compound statement**. It has the form $p \vee q$, where p is the statement "$2 < -7$" and q is the statement "$15 > 100$."

8. This sentence is six words long.

This is **not a statement** because it is self-referential. Self-referential sentences can cause problems. For example, observe that the negation of this sentence would be "This sentence is not six words long." The sentence and its negation both appear to be true. That would be a problem. It's a good thing they're not statements!

9. A triangle is equilateral if and only if all three sides of the triangle have the same length.

This is a **compound statement**. It has the form $p \leftrightarrow q$, where p is the statement "A triangle is equilateral," and q is the statement "All three sides of the triangle have the same length."

10. I cannot speak Russian, but I can speak Spanish.

This is a **compound statement**. It has the form $\neg p \wedge q$, where p is the statement "I speak Russian," and q is the statement "I can speak Spanish." Note that in sentential logic, the word "but" has the same meaning as the word "and." In English, the word "but" is used to introduce contrast with the part of the sentence that has already been mentioned. However, logically it is no different from "and."

What is the negation of each of the following statements?

11. Cauliflower is Jamie's favorite vegetable.

Cauliflower is not Jamie's favorite vegetable.

12. We have three cats.

We do not have three cats.

13. $15 < -12$.

$15 \geq -12$

Note: In words, $15 < -12$ can be read, "fifteen is less than negative twelve."

The negation of this statement is "fifteen is not less than negative twelve" (symbolically, we can write $15 \nless -12$). Using a basic property of the number systems we are most familiar with, $15 \nless -12$ is equivalent to $15 \geq -12$.

It follows that the negation of $15 < -12$ is equivalent to $15 \geq -12$.

14. You are not serious.

You are serious.

Note: Technically, the negation is "It is not the case that you are not serious." However, by the law of double negation, this is logically equivalent to "You are serious."

15. The function f is continuous.

The function f is not continuous.

16. The real number system with the standard topology is locally compact.

The real number system with the standard topology is not locally compact.

Let p represent the statement "5 is an odd integer," let q represent the statement "Brazil is in Europe," and let r represent the statement "A lobster is an insect." Rewrite each of the following symbolic statements in words, and state the truth value of each statement:

Note: p has truth value T, while q and r both have truth value F (a lobster is a crustacean, not an insect).

17. $p \lor q$

$p \lor q$ represents "**5 is an odd integer or Brazil is in Europe.**" Since p has truth value T, it follows that $p \lor q$ has truth value **T**.

18. $\neg r$

$\neg r$ represents "**A lobster is not an insect.**" Since r has truth value F, it follows that $\neg r$ has truth value **T**.

19. $p \rightarrow q$

$p \rightarrow q$ represents "**If 5 is an odd integer , then Brazil is in Europe.**" Since p has truth value T and q has truth value F, it follows that $p \rightarrow q$ has truth value **F**.

20. $p \leftrightarrow r$

$p \leftrightarrow r$ represents "**5 is an odd integer if and only if a lobster is an insect.**" Since p and r have opposite truth values, $p \leftrightarrow r$ has truth value **F**.

21. $\neg q \land r$

$\neg q \land r$ represents "**Brazil is not in Europe and a lobster is an insect.**" Since r has truth value F, it follows that $\neg q \land r$ has truth value **F**.

22. $\neg(p \land q)$

$\neg(p \land q)$ represents "**It is not the case that 5 is an odd integer and Brazil is in Europe.**" Since $p \land q$ has truth value F (because q has truth value F), it follows that $\neg(p \land q)$ has truth value **T**.

23. $\neg p \lor \neg q$

$\neg p \lor \neg q$ represents "**5 is not an odd integer or Brazil is not in Europe.**" Since $\neg q$ has truth value T (do you see why?), it follows that $\neg p \lor \neg q$ has truth value **T**.

24. $(p \land q) \rightarrow r$

$(p \land q) \rightarrow r$ represents "**If 5 is an odd integer and Brazil is in Europe, then a lobster is an insect.**" Since $p \land q$ has truth value F (because q has truth value F), it follows that $(p \land q) \rightarrow r$ has truth value **T**.

Consider the compound sentence "You can have a cookie or ice cream." In English this would most likely mean that you can have one or the other but not both. The word "or" used here is generally called an "exclusive or" because it excludes the possibility of both. The disjunction is an "inclusive or."

25. Using the symbol $\oplus$ for exclusive or, draw the truth table for this connective.

p	q	$p \oplus q$
T	T	F
T	F	T
F	T	T
F	F	F

26. Using only the logical connectives $\neg$, $\wedge$, and $\vee$, produce a statement using the propositional variables p and q that has the same truth values as $p \oplus q$.

We want to express that p is true or q is true, but p and q are not both true. Expressed in symbols, this is $(p \vee q) \wedge \neg(p \wedge q)$.

Note: (1) Let's check that $(p \vee q) \wedge \neg(p \wedge q)$ behaves as desired.

If p and q are both true, then $\neg(p \wedge q) \equiv F$, and so, $(p \vee q) \wedge \neg(p \wedge q) \equiv (p \vee q) \wedge F \equiv F$.

If p and q are both false, then $p \vee q \equiv F$, and so, $(p \vee q) \wedge \neg(p \wedge q) \equiv F \wedge \neg(p \wedge q) \equiv F$.

Finally, if p and q have opposite truth values, then $p \vee q \equiv T$ and $\neg(p \wedge q) \equiv T$ (because $p \wedge q \equiv F$). Therefore, $(p \vee q) \wedge \neg(p \wedge q) \equiv T \wedge T \equiv T$.

(2) Recall that the word "but" is logically the same as the word "and" (see Problem 10 above).

(3) Another way to see that $p \oplus q$ has the same truth values as $(p \vee q) \wedge \neg(p \wedge q)$ is to draw the truth tables for each and observe that row by row they have the same truth values. We do this below.

p	q	$p \oplus q$	$p \vee q$	$p \wedge q$	$\neg(p \wedge q)$	$(p \vee q) \wedge \neg(p \wedge q)$
T	T	F	T	T	F	F
T	F	T	T	F	T	T
F	T	T	T	F	T	T
F	F	F	F	F	T	F

Observe that the third column of the truth table corresponds to $p \oplus q$, the last (seventh) column corresponds to $(p \vee q) \wedge \neg(p \wedge q)$, and both these columns have the same truth values.

(4) In this problem, we showed that $p \oplus q \equiv (p \vee q) \wedge \neg(p \wedge q)$.

Consider the four distinct propositional variables p, q, r, and s.

27. How many different truth assignments are there for this list of propositional variables?

$2 \cdot 2 \cdot 2 \cdot 2 = \mathbf{16}$

28. How many different truth assignments are there for this list of propositional variables such that p is true and q is false?

$2 \cdot 2 = \mathbf{4}$

29. How many different truth assignments are there for this list of propositional variables such that q, r, and s are all true?

$\mathbf{2}$

30. How many different truth assignments are there for a list of 5 propositional variables?

$2 \cdot 2 \cdot 2 \cdot 2 \cdot 2 = \mathbf{32}$

Let p, q, and r represent true statements. Compute the truth value of each of the following compound statements:

31. $(p \vee q) \vee r$

Detailed solution: $(p \vee q) \vee r \equiv (T \vee T) \vee T \equiv T \vee T \equiv \mathbf{T}$.

Quicker solution: $(p \vee q) \vee r \equiv (p \vee q) \vee T \equiv \mathbf{T}$.

32. $(p \vee q) \wedge \neg r$

Detailed solution: $(p \vee q) \wedge \neg r \equiv (T \vee T) \wedge \neg T \equiv T \wedge F \equiv \mathbf{F}$.

Quicker solution: $(p \vee q) \wedge \neg r \equiv (p \vee q) \wedge F \equiv \mathbf{F}$.

33. $\neg p \rightarrow (q \vee r)$

Detailed solution: $\neg p \rightarrow (q \vee r) \equiv \neg T \rightarrow (T \vee T) \equiv F \rightarrow T \equiv \mathbf{T}$.

Quicker solution: $\neg p \rightarrow (q \vee r) \equiv F \rightarrow (q \vee r) \equiv \mathbf{T}$.

34. $\neg(p \leftrightarrow \neg q) \wedge r$

Detailed solution: $\neg(p \leftrightarrow \neg q) \wedge r \equiv \neg(T \leftrightarrow \neg T) \wedge T \equiv \neg(T \leftrightarrow F) \wedge T \equiv \neg F \wedge T \equiv T \wedge T \equiv \mathbf{T}$.

Quicker solution: $\neg(p \leftrightarrow \neg q) \wedge r \equiv \neg(T \leftrightarrow F) \wedge T \equiv \neg F \wedge T \equiv T \wedge T \equiv \mathbf{T}$.

35. $\neg[p \wedge (\neg q \to r)]$

Detailed solution: $\neg[p \wedge (\neg q \to r)] \equiv \neg[T \wedge (\neg T \to T)] \equiv \neg[T \wedge (F \to T)] \equiv \neg[T \wedge T] \equiv \neg T \equiv \textbf{F}$.

Quicker solution: $\neg[p \wedge (\neg q \to r)] \equiv \neg[p \wedge (F \to r)] \equiv \neg[p \wedge T] \equiv \neg[T \wedge T] \equiv \neg T \equiv \textbf{F}$.

36. $\neg[(\neg p \vee \neg q) \leftrightarrow \neg r]$

Detailed solution:
$\neg[(\neg p \vee \neg q) \leftrightarrow \neg r] \equiv \neg[(\neg T \vee \neg T) \leftrightarrow \neg T] \equiv \neg[(F \vee F) \leftrightarrow F] \equiv \neg[F \leftrightarrow F] \equiv \neg T \equiv \textbf{F}$.

Quicker solution: $\neg[(\neg p \vee \neg q) \leftrightarrow \neg r] \equiv \neg[F \leftrightarrow F] \equiv \neg T \equiv \textbf{F}$.

37. $p \to (q \to \neg r)$

Detailed solution: $p \to (q \to \neg r) \equiv T \to (T \to \neg T) \equiv T \to (T \to F) \equiv T \to F \equiv \textbf{F}$.

Quicker solution: $p \to (q \to \neg r) \equiv T \to (T \to F) \equiv T \to F \equiv \textbf{F}$.

38. $\neg[\neg p \to (q \to \neg r)]$

Detailed solution:
$\neg[\neg p \to (q \to \neg r)] \equiv \neg[\neg T \to (T \to \neg T)] \equiv \neg[F \to (T \to F)] \equiv \neg[F \to F] \equiv \neg T \equiv \textbf{F}$.

Quicker solution: $\neg[\neg p \to (q \to \neg r)] \equiv \neg[F \to (q \to \neg r)] \equiv \neg T \equiv \textbf{F}$.

Determine if each of the following statements is a tautology, a contradiction, or neither.

39. $p \wedge p$

If $p \equiv T$, then $p \wedge p \equiv T \wedge T \equiv T$. If $p \equiv F$, then $p \wedge p \equiv F \wedge F \equiv F$. **Neither**

40. $p \wedge \neg p$

$p \wedge \neg p \equiv F$. **Contradiction**

41. $(p \vee \neg p) \to (p \wedge \neg p)$

$(p \vee \neg p) \to (p \wedge \neg p) \equiv T \to F \equiv F$. **Contradiction**

42. $\neg(p \vee q) \leftrightarrow (\neg p \wedge \neg q)$

Since $\neg(p \vee q) \equiv \neg p \wedge \neg q$ (De Morgan's law), $\neg(p \vee q) \leftrightarrow (\neg p \wedge \neg q)$ is a **Tautology**.

43. $p \to (\neg q \wedge r)$

If $p \equiv F$, then we have $p \to (\neg q \wedge r) \equiv F \to (\neg q \wedge r) \equiv T$. If $p \equiv T$ and $r \equiv F$, then we have $p \to (\neg q \wedge r) \equiv T \to (\neg q \wedge F) \equiv T \to F \equiv F$. **Neither**

44. $(p \leftrightarrow q) \to (p \to q)$

If p and q have the same truth value, then we have $p \leftrightarrow q \equiv T$ and $p \rightarrow q \equiv T$, and therefore, $(p \leftrightarrow q) \rightarrow (p \rightarrow q) \equiv T \rightarrow T \equiv T$. If p and q have opposite truth values, then $p \leftrightarrow q \equiv F$, and therefore, we have $(p \leftrightarrow q) \rightarrow (p \rightarrow q) \equiv F \rightarrow (p \rightarrow q) \equiv T$. Since all possible truth assignments of the propositional variables lead to a truth value of T, $(p \leftrightarrow q) \rightarrow (p \rightarrow q)$ is a **Tautology**.

LEVEL 4

Assume that the given compound statement is true. Determine the truth value of each propositional variable.

45. $p \wedge q$

If $p \equiv F$ or $q \equiv F$, then $p \wedge q \equiv F$. Therefore, $\boldsymbol{p} \equiv \mathbf{T}$ and $\boldsymbol{q} \equiv \mathbf{T}$.

46. $\neg(p \rightarrow q)$

Since $\neg(p \rightarrow q)$ is true, $p \rightarrow q$ is false. Therefore, $\boldsymbol{p} \equiv \mathbf{T}$ and $\boldsymbol{q} \equiv \mathbf{F}$.

47. $p \leftrightarrow [\neg(p \wedge q)]$

If $p \equiv F$, then $p \wedge q \equiv F$, and so, $p \leftrightarrow [\neg(p \wedge q)] \equiv F \leftrightarrow T \equiv F$. So, $\boldsymbol{p} \equiv \mathbf{T}$. It follows that $\neg(p \wedge q) \equiv T$, and so $p \wedge q \equiv F$. Since $p \equiv T$, we must have $\boldsymbol{q} \equiv \mathbf{F}$.

48. $[p \wedge (q \vee r)] \wedge \neg r$

As in Problem 45, we must have $p \wedge (q \vee r) \equiv T$ and $\neg r \equiv T$. So, $\boldsymbol{p} \equiv \mathbf{T}$, $q \vee r \equiv T$, and $\boldsymbol{r} \equiv \mathbf{F}$. Since $q \vee r \equiv T$ and $r \equiv F$, we must have $\boldsymbol{q} \equiv \mathbf{T}$.

Let p represent a true statement. Decide if this is enough information to determine the truth value of each of the following statements. If so, state that truth value.

49. $p \vee q$

$(p \vee q) \equiv T \vee q \equiv \mathbf{T}$.

50. $p \rightarrow q$

$p \rightarrow q \equiv T \rightarrow q$. If $q \equiv T$, we get $T \rightarrow T \equiv T$. If $q \equiv F$, we get $T \rightarrow F \equiv F$. **There is not enough information**.

51. $\neg p \rightarrow \neg(q \vee \neg r)$

$\neg p \rightarrow \neg(q \vee \neg r) \equiv F \rightarrow \neg(q \vee \neg r) \equiv \mathbf{T}$.

52. $\neg(\neg p \wedge q) \leftrightarrow p$

$\neg(\neg p \wedge q) \leftrightarrow p \equiv \neg(F \wedge q) \leftrightarrow T \equiv \neg F \leftrightarrow T \equiv T \leftrightarrow T \equiv \mathbf{T}$.

53. $(p \leftrightarrow q) \leftrightarrow \neg p$

$(p \leftrightarrow q) \leftrightarrow \neg p \equiv (\text{T} \leftrightarrow q) \leftrightarrow \text{F}$. If $q \equiv \text{T}$, we get $(\text{T} \leftrightarrow \text{T}) \leftrightarrow \text{F} \equiv \text{T} \leftrightarrow \text{F} \equiv \text{F}$. If $q \equiv \text{F}$, we get $(\text{T} \leftrightarrow \text{F}) \leftrightarrow \text{F} \equiv \text{F} \leftrightarrow \text{F} \equiv \text{T}$. **There is not enough information.**

54. $\neg[(\neg p \wedge \neg q) \leftrightarrow \neg r]$

$\neg[(\neg p \wedge \neg q) \leftrightarrow \neg r] \equiv \neg[(\text{F} \wedge \neg q) \leftrightarrow \neg r] \equiv \neg(\text{F} \leftrightarrow \neg r)$. If $r \equiv \text{T}$, we get $\neg \text{T} \equiv \text{F}$. If $r \equiv \text{F}$, we get $\neg \text{F} \equiv \text{T}$. **There is not enough information.**

55. $[(p \wedge \neg p) \to p] \wedge (p \vee \neg p)$

$[(p \wedge \neg p) \to p] \wedge (p \vee \neg p) \equiv [(\text{T} \wedge \text{F}) \to \text{T}] \wedge (\text{T} \vee \text{F}) \equiv [\text{F} \to \text{T}] \wedge \text{T} \equiv \text{T} \wedge \text{T} \equiv \textbf{T}.$

56. $r \to [\neg q \to (\neg p \to \neg r)]$

$r \to [\neg q \to (\neg p \to \neg r)] \equiv r \to [\neg q \to (\text{F} \to \neg r)] \equiv r \to [\neg q \to \text{T}] \equiv r \to \text{T} \equiv \textbf{T}.$

For each of the following pairs of statements A and B, show that $A \equiv B$.

57. $A = p \wedge q, B = q \wedge p$

Draw the truth tables.

58. $A = (p \vee q) \vee r, B = p \vee (q \vee r)$

Draw truth tables.

59. $A = p \wedge (q \vee r), B = (p \wedge q) \vee (p \wedge r)$

Draw truth tables.

60. $A = (p \vee q) \wedge p, B = p$

If $p \equiv \text{T}$, then $p \vee q \equiv \text{T} \vee q \equiv \text{T}$. So, $A \equiv \text{T} \wedge \text{T} \equiv \text{T}$. Also, $B \equiv \text{T}$. If $p \equiv \text{F}$, then $A \equiv (p \vee q) \wedge \text{F} \equiv \text{F}$ and $B \equiv \text{F}$. So, all four possible truth assignments of p and q lead to the same truth value for ϕ and ψ. It follows that $\phi \equiv \psi$.

Note: We have just proved the first **absorption law.**

61. $A = p \leftrightarrow q, B = (p \to q) \wedge (q \to p)$

If $p \equiv \text{T}$, then we have $A \equiv \text{T} \leftrightarrow q \equiv q, B \equiv (\text{T} \to q) \wedge (q \to \text{T}) \equiv q \wedge \text{T} \equiv q$. If $p \equiv \text{F}$, then we have $A \equiv \text{F} \leftrightarrow q \equiv \neg q, B \equiv (\text{F} \to q) \wedge (q \to \text{F}) \equiv \text{T} \wedge \neg q \equiv \neg q$. So, all four possible truth assignments of p and q lead to the same truth value for A and B. It follows that $A \equiv B$.

Note: We have just proved the **law of the biconditional.**

62. $A = \neg(p \to q), B = p \wedge \neg q$

If $p \equiv F$, then we have $A \equiv \neg(F \to q) \equiv \neg T \equiv F$, $B \equiv F \wedge \neg q \equiv F$. If $q \equiv T$, then we have $A \equiv \neg(p \to T) \equiv \neg T \equiv F$, $B \equiv p \wedge \neg T \equiv p \wedge F \equiv F$. Finally, if $p \equiv T$ and $q \equiv F$, then we have $A \equiv \neg(T \to F) \equiv \neg F \equiv T$, $B \equiv T \wedge \neg F \equiv T \wedge T \equiv T$. So, all four possible truth assignments of p and q lead to the same truth value for A and B. It follows that $A \equiv B$.

Simplify each statement.

63. $p \vee (p \wedge \neg p)$

$p \vee (p \wedge \neg p) \equiv p \vee F \equiv \boldsymbol{p}$.

64. $(p \wedge q) \vee \neg p$

$(p \wedge q) \vee \neg p \equiv (p \vee \neg p) \wedge (q \vee \neg p) \equiv T \wedge (q \vee \neg p) \equiv q \vee \neg p \equiv \boldsymbol{\neg p \vee q}$.

65. $\neg p \to (\neg q \to p)$

$\neg p \to (\neg q \to p) \equiv p \vee (\neg q \to p) \equiv p \vee (q \vee p) \equiv p \vee (p \vee q) \equiv (p \vee p) \vee q \equiv \boldsymbol{p \vee q}$.

66. $(p \wedge \neg q) \vee p$

$(p \wedge \neg q) \vee p \equiv \boldsymbol{p}$ (Absorption).

67. $[(q \wedge p) \vee q] \wedge [(q \vee p) \wedge p]$

$[(q \wedge p) \vee q] \wedge [(q \vee p) \wedge p] \equiv [(q \wedge p) \vee q] \wedge [(p \vee q) \wedge p] \equiv q \wedge p$ (Absorption) $\equiv \boldsymbol{p \wedge q}$.

LEVEL 5

Without drawing a truth table or using List 1.28, show that each of the following is a tautology.

68. $[p \wedge (q \vee r)] \leftrightarrow [(p \wedge q) \vee (p \wedge r)]$

If $p \equiv F$, then $p \wedge (q \vee r) \equiv F$, $p \wedge q \equiv F$, and $p \wedge r \equiv F$. So, $(p \wedge q) \vee (p \wedge r) \equiv F$. It follows that $[p \wedge (q \vee r)] \leftrightarrow [(p \wedge q) \vee (p \wedge r)] \equiv F \leftrightarrow F \equiv \mathbf{T}$.

If $p \equiv T$ and $q \equiv T$, then $p \wedge (q \vee r) \equiv T \wedge T \equiv T$ and $(p \wedge q) \vee (p \wedge r) \equiv T \vee (p \wedge r) \equiv T$. It follows that $[p \wedge (q \vee r)] \leftrightarrow [(p \wedge q) \vee (p \wedge r)] \equiv T \leftrightarrow T \equiv \mathbf{T}$.

If $p \equiv T$ and $q \equiv F$, then $p \wedge (q \vee r) \equiv T \wedge r \equiv r$ and $(p \wedge q) \vee (p \wedge r) \equiv F \vee r \equiv r$. It follows that $[p \wedge (q \vee r)] \leftrightarrow [(p \wedge q) \vee (p \wedge r)] \equiv r \leftrightarrow r \equiv \mathbf{T}$.

Notes: (1) We can display this reasoning visually as follows:

$$[p \wedge (q \vee r)] \leftrightarrow [(p \wedge q) \vee (p \wedge r)]$$

F F		**T**	F F	F	F F	
T T T T		**T**	T T T	T		
T r F r		**T**	T F F	r	T r	

Each row of truth values is placed in the order suggested by the solution above. For example, for the first row, we start by writing F under each p because we are assuming that $p \equiv$ F. Next, since the conjunction of F with anything else is F, we write F under each $\wedge$ (there are three that appear). Next, since F $\vee$ F $\equiv$ F, we write F under the rightmost $\vee$. Finally, since F $\leftrightarrow$ F $\equiv$ T, we write T under $\leftrightarrow$. This is the truth value of the entire statement, and therefore, we are done with the case $p \equiv$ F. The other two rows work the same way.

(2) We used two of the identity laws in the third part of the solution: T $\wedge r \equiv r$ and F $\vee r \equiv r$.

69. $\left[[(p \wedge q) \to r] \to s\right] \to [(p \to r) \to s]$

If $s \equiv$ T, then $(p \to r) \to s \equiv$ T, and therefore, $\left[[(p \wedge q) \to r] \to s\right] \to [(p \to r) \to s] \equiv$ **T.**

Now, assume $s \equiv$ F, and either $p \equiv$ F or $q \equiv$ F. Then $p \wedge q \equiv$ F, and so $(p \wedge q) \to r \equiv$ T. Therefore, $[(p \wedge q) \to r] \to s \equiv$ F, and so, $\left[[(p \wedge q) \to r] \to s\right] \to [(p \to r) \to s] \equiv$ **T.**

Finally, assume $s \equiv$ F, $p \equiv$ T, and $q \equiv$ T. Then $p \wedge q \equiv$ T, and so, $(p \wedge q) \to r \equiv r$. Therefore, $[(p \wedge q) \to r] \to s \equiv \neg r$. Also, $p \to r \equiv r$, and so $(p \to r) \to s \equiv \neg r$. So, we get $\neg r \to \neg r \equiv$ **T.**

Note: The dedicated reader should display this reasoning visually, as was done in Note 1 following the solution to Problem 68 above.

Let n be a positive integer (in other words, n is one of the numbers $1, 2, 3, 4, ...$) and let A be a statement involving n propositional variables. Determine how many rows are in the truth table for A if n is equal to each of the following:

70. $n = 6$

$2 \cdot 2 \cdot 2 \cdot 2 \cdot 2 \cdot 2 = 2^6 = \mathbf{64}$

71. $n = 10$

$2 \cdot 2 \cdot 2 \cdot 2 \cdot 2 \cdot 2 \cdot 2 \cdot 2 \cdot 2 \cdot 2 = 2^{10} = \mathbf{1024}$

72. n is an arbitrary positive integer (provide an explicit expression involving n.)

$\mathbf{2^n}$

Problem Set 2

LEVEL 1

Determine whether each of the following statements is true or false:

1. $b \in \{b\}$

$\{b\}$ has exactly 1 element, namely b. So, $b \in \{b\}$ is **true**.

2. $15 \in \{0, 5, 10, 15\}$

$\{0, 5, 10, 15\}$ has exactly 4 elements, namely 0, 5, 10, and 15. In particular, $15 \in \{0, 5, 10, 15\}$ is **true**.

3. $-11 \in \{11\}$

$\{11\}$ has exactly 1 element, namely 11. So, $-11 \notin \{11\}$. Therefore, $-11 \in \{11\}$ is **false**.

4. $0 \in \mathbb{Z}$

$\mathbb{Z} = \{\dots, -4, -3, -2, -1, 0, 1, 2, 3, 4, \dots\}$. In particular, $0 \in \mathbb{Z}$ is **true**.

5. $-18 \in \mathbb{N}$

$\mathbb{N} = \{0, 1, 2, 3, \dots\}$. Therefore, $-18 \in \mathbb{N}$ is **false**.

6. $\frac{23}{5} \in \mathbb{Q}$

Since $23, 5 \in \mathbb{Z}$ and $5 \neq 0$, $\frac{23}{5} \in \mathbb{Q}$ is **true**.

7. $\emptyset \subseteq \{x, y, z, w\}$

The empty set is a subset of every set. So, $\emptyset \subseteq \{x, y, z, w\}$ is **true**.

8. $\{\Delta\} \subseteq \{\square, \Delta\}$

The only element of $\{\Delta\}$ is Δ. Since Δ is also an element of $\{\square, \Delta\}$, $\{\Delta\} \subseteq \{\square, \Delta\}$ is **true**.

9. $\{a, b, c, d\} \subset \{a, b, c, d\}$

No set is a **proper** subset of itself. So, $\{a, b, c, d\} \subset \{a, b, c, d\}$ is **false**.

10. $\{0, 1, \{2, 3\}\} \subseteq \{0, 1, 2, 3\}$

$\{2, 3\} \in \{0, 1, \{2,3\}\}$, but $\{2, 3\} \notin \{0, 1, 2, 3\}$. So, $\{0, 1, \{2,3\}\} \subseteq \{0, 1, 2, 3\}$ is **false**.

Determine the cardinality of each of the following sets:

11. {apple, banana, watermelon}

|{apple, banana, watermelon}| = **3**.

12. $\{3, 6, 10, 17, 23\}$

$|\{3, 6, 10, 17, 23\}| = \mathbf{5}$.

13. $\{1, 2, \dots, 87\}$

$|\{1, 2, \dots, 87\}| = \mathbf{87}$.

14. $\left\{\frac{1}{2}, \frac{1}{3}, \dots, \frac{1}{10}\right\}$

$\left|\left\{\frac{1}{2}, \frac{1}{3}, \dots, \frac{1}{10}\right\}\right| = \mathbf{9}$.

Provide an example of a set X with the given properties:

15. (i) $X \subset \mathbb{Z}$ (X is a *proper* subset of $\mathbb{Z}$); (ii) X is infinite; (iii) X contains both positive and negative integers; (iv) X contains both even and odd integers.

One example of such a set X is $X = \{\dots, \mathbf{-6}, \mathbf{-4}, \mathbf{-2}, \mathbf{1}, \mathbf{3}, \mathbf{5}, \dots\}$.

16. (i) $X \subset \mathbb{R}$ (X is a *proper* subset of $\mathbb{R}$); (ii) X contains both rational and irrational numbers.

One example of such a set X is $X = \{\mathbf{0.1}, \mathbf{0.101001000100001}\dots\}$.

17. (i) $X \subset \mathbb{C}$ (X is a *proper* subset of $\mathbb{C}$); (ii) X is infinite; (iii) X contains real numbers; and (iv) X contains complex numbers that are not real.

One example of such a set X is $X = \{\boldsymbol{a} + \boldsymbol{b}\boldsymbol{i} \mid \boldsymbol{a} \in \mathbb{R} \land (\boldsymbol{b} = \mathbf{0} \lor \boldsymbol{b} = \mathbf{1})\}$.

Let $A = \{x, y, z, w\}$ and $B = \{s, t, y, w\}$. Determine each of the following:

18. $A \cup B$

$A \cup B = \{\boldsymbol{x}, \boldsymbol{y}, \boldsymbol{z}, \boldsymbol{w}, \boldsymbol{s}, \boldsymbol{t}\}$

19. $A \cap B$

$A \cap B = \{\boldsymbol{y}, \boldsymbol{w}\}$

20. $A \setminus B$

$A \setminus B = \{\boldsymbol{x}, \boldsymbol{z}\}$

21. $B \setminus A$

$B \setminus A = \{s, t\}$

22. $A \triangle B$

$A \triangle B = (A \setminus B) \cup (B \setminus A) = \{x, z\} \cup \{s, t\} = \{x, z, s, t\}$

LEVEL 2

Determine whether each of the following statements is true or false:

23. $3 \in \emptyset$

The empty set has no elements. So, $x \in \emptyset$ is false for any x. In particular, $3 \in \emptyset$ is **false**.

24. $\emptyset \in \emptyset$

The empty set has no elements. So, $x \in \emptyset$ is false for any x. In particular, $\emptyset \in \emptyset$ is **false**.

25. $\emptyset \in \{\emptyset, \{\emptyset\}\}$

The set $\{\emptyset, \{\emptyset\}\}$ has exactly 2 element, namely $\emptyset$ and $\{\emptyset\}$. In particular, $\emptyset \in \{\emptyset\}$ is **true**.

26. $\{\emptyset\} \in \emptyset$

The empty set has no elements. So, $x \in \emptyset$ is false for any x. In particular, $\{\emptyset\} \in \emptyset$ is **false**.

27. $\{\emptyset\} \in \{\emptyset\}$

The set $\{\emptyset\}$ has 1 element, namely $\emptyset$. Since $\{\emptyset\} \neq \emptyset$, $\{\emptyset\} \in \{\emptyset\}$ is **false**.

28. $7 \in \{5k \mid k = 1, 2, 3, 4, 5, 6, 7\}$

$\{5k \mid k = 1, 2, 3, 4, 5, 6, 7\} = \{5, 10, 15, 20, 25, 30, 35\}$. So, $7 \notin \{5k \mid k = 1, 2, 3, 4, 5, 6, 7\}$. Therefore, it follows that $7 \in \{5k \mid k = 1, 2, 3, 4, 5, 6, 7\}$ is **false**.

29. $13 \in 2\mathbb{N}$

$2\mathbb{N} = \{0, 2, 4, 6, 8, 10, 12, 14, \ldots\}$. In particular, $13 \in 2\mathbb{N}$ is **false**.

30. $\emptyset \subseteq \emptyset$

The empty set is a subset of every set. So, $\emptyset \subseteq X$ is true for any X. In particular, $\emptyset \subseteq \emptyset$ is **true**. (This can also be done by using the fact that every set is a subset of itself.)

31. $\emptyset \subseteq \{\emptyset\}$

Again, (as in Problem 30), $\emptyset \subseteq X$ is true for any X. In particular, $\emptyset \subseteq \{\emptyset\}$ is **true**.

19

32. $\{\emptyset\} \subseteq \emptyset$

The only subset of $\emptyset$ is $\emptyset$. So, $\{\emptyset\} \subseteq \emptyset$ is **false**.

33. $\{\emptyset\} \subseteq \{\emptyset\}$

Every set is a subset of itself. So, $\{\emptyset\} \subseteq \{\emptyset\}$ is **true**.

Determine the cardinality of each of the following sets:

34. $\{0, 0, 1, 2, 2, 2, 3, 3\}$

$\{0, 0, 1, 2, 2, 2, 3, 3\} = \{0, 1, 2, 3\}$. Therefore, $|\{0, 0, 1, 2, 2, 2, 3, 3\}| = |\{0, 1, 2, 3\}| = \mathbf{4}$.

35. $\{\{0, 1\}, \{2, 3, 4\}\}$

$\{\{0, 1\}, \{2, 3, 4\}\}$ consists of the 2 elements $\{0, 1\}$ and $\{2, 3, 4\}$. So, $|\{\{0, 1\}, \{2, 3, 4\}\}| = \mathbf{2}$.

36. $\{3, 4, 5, \dots, 2379, 2380\}$

$|\{3, 4, 5, \dots, 2379, 2380\}| = 2380 - 3 + 1 = \mathbf{2378}$ (notice that we used the fence-post formula here).

Let $A = \{\emptyset, \{\emptyset, \{\emptyset\}\}\}$ and $B = \{\emptyset, \{\emptyset\}\}$. Compute each of the following:

37. $A \cup B$

$A \cup B = \{\emptyset, \{\emptyset\}, \{\emptyset, \{\emptyset\}\}\}$

38. $A \cap B$

$A \cap B = \{\emptyset\}$

39. $A \setminus B$

$A \setminus B = \{\{\emptyset, \{\emptyset\}\}\}$

40. $B \setminus A$

$B \setminus A = \{\{\emptyset\}\}$

41. $A \triangle B$

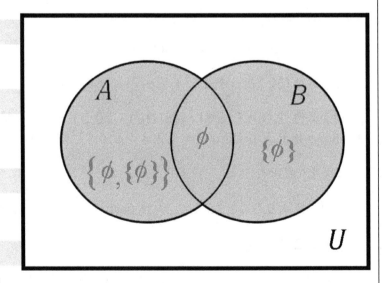

$A \triangle B = \{\{\emptyset, \{\emptyset\}\}\} \cup \{\{\emptyset\}\} = \{\{\emptyset\}, \{\emptyset, \{\emptyset\}\}\}$

Determine if each of the following real numbers is rational or irrational:

42. $1.\overline{3}$

rational (repeating decimal)

43. − 246.810121416182022242628 …

irrational

44. 987.65432154321543215432154321 …

rational (987.65432154321543215432154321 … = $987.6\overline{54321}$, repeating decimal)

45. 0

rational (terminating decimal)

LEVEL 3

Use set-builder notation to describe each of the following sets.

46. $\{1, 3, 5, 7, 9, 11, 13, 15\}$

$\{1, 3, 5, 7, 9, 1, 13, 15\} = \{n \in \mathbb{N} \mid n \text{ is odd} \wedge 1 \leq n \leq 15\}$

47. $2\mathbb{N}$

$2\mathbb{N} = \{n \in \mathbb{N} \mid n \text{ is even}\}$

48. $\mathbb{R} \setminus \mathbb{Q}$

$\mathbb{R} \setminus \mathbb{Q} = \{x \in \mathbb{R} \mid x \text{ is irrational}\}$

Determine the cardinality of each of the following sets:

49. $\left\{\{\{a, b\}\}\right\}$

The only element of $\left\{\{\{a, b\}\}\right\}$ is $\{\{a, b\}\}$. So, $\left|\left\{\{\{a, b\}\}\right\}\right| = 1$.

50. $\left\{\{0, 1\}, 0, \{0\}, \{0, \{0, 1, 2\}\}\right\}$

The elements of $\left\{\{0, 1\}, 0, \{0\}, \{0, \{0, 1, 2\}\}\right\}$ are $\{0, 1\}$, 0, $\{0\}$, and $\{0, \{0, 1, 2\}\}$. So, we see that $\left|\left\{\{0, 1\}, 0, \{0\}, \{0, \{0, 1, 2\}\}\right\}\right| = 4.$

51. $\left\{a, \{a\}, \{a, a\}, \{a, a, a, a\}, \{a, a, \{a\}\}, \{a, \{a\}, \{a\}\}\right\}$

$$\left\{a, \{a\}, \{a, a\}, \{a, a, a, a\}, \{a, a, \{a\}\}, \{a, \{a\}, \{a\}\}\right\}$$

$$= \{a, \{a\}, \{a\}, \{a\}, \{a, \{a\}\}, \{a, \{a\}\}\}$$
$$= \{a, \{a\}, \{a, \{a\}\}\}.$$

So, $\left|\{a, \{a\}, \{a, a\}, \{a, a, a, a\}, \{a, a, \{a\}\}, \{a, \{a\}, \{a\}\}\}\right| = \left|\{a, \{a\}, \{a, \{a\}\}\}\right| = \mathbf{3}$.

For each set X, determine $|\mathcal{P}(X)|$

52. $X = \{a, b, c, d, e\}$

Since $|X| = 5$, $|\mathcal{P}(X)| = 2^5 = \mathbf{32}$.

53. $X = \{\emptyset, \{\emptyset\}, \{\emptyset, \{\emptyset\}\}\}$

Since $|X| = 3$, $|\mathcal{P}(X)| = 2^3 = \mathbf{8}$.

54. $X = \{17, 18, 19, \dots, 102, 103\}$

Since $|X| = 103 - 17 + 1 = 87$, $|\mathcal{P}(X)| = \mathbf{2^{87}}$.

Let $A, B,$ and C be sets, let $X = (A \setminus B) \setminus C$, and let $Y = A \setminus (B \setminus C)$.

55. Draw Venn Diagrams for X and Y.

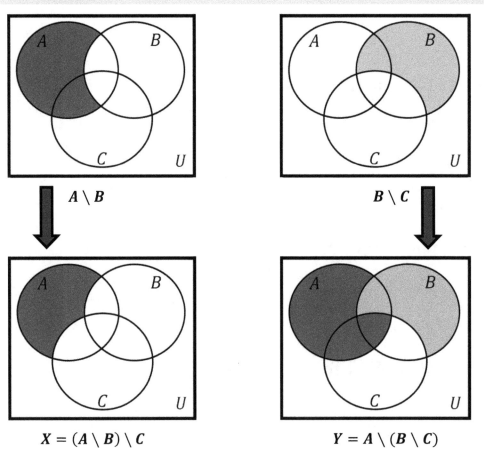

$A \setminus B$

$B \setminus C$

$X = (A \setminus B) \setminus C$

$Y = A \setminus (B \setminus C)$

22

56. Is $X \subseteq Y$?

Yes

57. Is $Y \subseteq X$?

No

58. Is $X = Y$?

No

LEVEL 4

Determine whether each of the following statements is true or false:

59. $0 \in \{0, \{1\}\}$

The set $\{0, \{1\}\}$ has exactly 2 elements, namely 0 and $\{1\}$. So, $0 \in \{0, \{1\}\}$ is **true**.

60. $\{b\} \in \{a, b\}$

The set $\{a, b\}$ has exactly 2 elements, namely a and b. So, $\{b\} \in \{a, b\}$ is **false**.

61. $\{1\} \in \{\{1\}, x, 2, y\}$

The set $\{\{1\}, x, 2, y\}$ has exactly 4 elements, namely $\{1\}$, x, 2 , and y. So, $\{1\} \in \{\{1\}, x, 2, y\}$ is **true**.

62. $\emptyset \in \{\{\emptyset\}\}$

The set $\{\{\emptyset\}\}$ has exactly 1 element, namely $\{\emptyset\}$. Since $\emptyset$ is not equal to $\{\emptyset\}$, $\emptyset \in \{\{\emptyset\}\}$ is **false**.

63. $\{\{\emptyset\}\} \in \emptyset$

The empty set has no elements. So, $x \in \emptyset$ is false for any x. In particular, $\{\{\emptyset\}\} \in \emptyset$ is **false**.

Compute the power set of each of the following sets:

64. $\emptyset$

$\mathcal{P}(\emptyset) = \{\emptyset\}$

65. $\{0\}$

$\mathcal{P}(\{0\}) = \{\emptyset, \{0\}\}$

66. $\{cat, dog\}$

$\mathcal{P}(\{\text{cat}, \text{dog}\}) = \{\emptyset, \{\text{cat}\}, \{\text{dog}\}, \{\text{cat}, \text{dog}\}\}$

67. $\{\emptyset, \{\emptyset\}\}$

$\mathcal{P}(\{\emptyset, \{\emptyset\}\}) = \{\emptyset, \{\emptyset\}, \{\{\emptyset\}\}, \{\emptyset, \{\emptyset\}\}\}$

68. $\{\{\emptyset\}\}$

$\mathcal{P}(\{\{\emptyset\}\}) = \{\emptyset, \{\{\emptyset\}\}\}$

A relation R is **reflexive** if for all x, we have xRx. A relation R is **symmetric** if for all x, y, we have $xRy \rightarrow yRx$. A relation R is **transitive** if for all x, y, z, we have $(xRy \wedge yRz) \rightarrow xRz$. For example, the relation "=" is reflexive, symmetric, and transitive because for all x, we have $x = x$, for all x, y, we have $x = y \rightarrow y = x$, and for all x, y, z, we have $(x = y \wedge y = z) \rightarrow x = z$.

69. Is $\subseteq$ reflexive?

Yes. Every set is a subset of itself ($A \subseteq A$).

70. Is $\in$ reflexive?

No. Since the empty set has no elements, $\emptyset \notin \emptyset$. This **counterexample** shows that $\in$ is not reflexive.

71. Is $\subseteq$ symmetric?

No. $\{1\} \subseteq \{1, 2\}$, but $\{1, 2\} \nsubseteq \{1\}$. This **counterexample** shows that $\subseteq$ is not symmetric.

72. Is $\in$ symmetric?

No. $\emptyset \in \{\emptyset\}$, but $\{\emptyset\} \notin \emptyset$. This **counterexample** shows that $\in$ is not symmetric.

73. Is $\subseteq$ transitive?

Yes. If $A \subseteq B$ and $B \subseteq C$, then $A \subseteq C$.

74. Is $\in$ transitive?

No. $\emptyset \in \{\emptyset\} \in \{\{\emptyset\}\}$, but $\emptyset \notin \{\{\emptyset\}\}$. This **counterexample** shows that $\in$ is not transitive.

LEVEL 5

We say that a set A is **transitive** if every element of A is a subset of A. Determine if each of the following sets is transitive:

75. $\emptyset$

Since $\emptyset$ has no elements, $\emptyset$ **is transitive**. (The statement "$x \in \emptyset \rightarrow x \subseteq \emptyset$" is true simply because "$x \in \emptyset$" is always false. In other words, the statement is vacuously true.)

76. $\{\emptyset\}$

The only element of $\{\emptyset\}$ is $\emptyset$, and $\emptyset \subseteq \{\emptyset\}$ is true. So, $\{\emptyset\}$ **is transitive**.

77. $\{\{\emptyset\}\}$

$\{\emptyset\} \in \{\{\emptyset\}\}$ and $\emptyset \in \{\emptyset\}$, but $\emptyset \notin \{\{\emptyset\}\}$. So, $\{\{\emptyset\}\}$ **is not transitive**.

78. $\{\emptyset, \{\emptyset\}\}$

$\{\emptyset, \{\emptyset\}\}$ has 2 elements, namely $\emptyset$ and $\{\emptyset\}$. Both sets are subsets of $\{\emptyset, \{\emptyset\}\}$. It follows that $\{\emptyset, \{\emptyset\}\}$ **is transitive**.

79. $\{\emptyset, \{\emptyset\}, \{\{\emptyset\}\}\}$

$\{\emptyset, \{\emptyset\}, \{\{\emptyset\}\}\}$ has 3 elements, namely $\emptyset$, $\{\emptyset\}$, and $\{\{\emptyset\}\}$. All three of these sets are subsets of $\{\emptyset, \{\emptyset\}, \{\{\emptyset\}\}\}$. It follows that $\{\emptyset, \{\emptyset\}, \{\{\emptyset\}\}\}$ **is transitive**.

80. $\{\{\emptyset\}, \{\emptyset, \{\emptyset\}\}\}$

$\{\emptyset\} \in \{\{\emptyset\}, \{\emptyset, \{\emptyset\}\}\}$ and $\emptyset \in \{\emptyset\}$, but $\emptyset \notin \{\{\emptyset\}, \{\emptyset, \{\emptyset\}\}\}$. So, $\{\{\emptyset\}, \{\emptyset, \{\emptyset\}\}\}$ **is not transitive**.

81. Assuming that A is transitive, is $\mathcal{P}(A)$ transitive?

Yes. To see this, let $x \in \mathcal{P}(A)$, and let $y \in x$. Since $x \in \mathcal{P}(A)$, $x \subseteq A$. Since $y \in x$ and $x \subseteq A$, $y \in A$. Since A is transitive and $y \in A$, $y \subseteq A$. So, $y \in \mathcal{P}(A)$. Since $y \in x$ was arbitrary, $x \subseteq \mathcal{P}(A)$. Therefore, every element of $\mathcal{P}(A)$ is a subset of $\mathcal{P}(A)$. So, $\mathcal{P}(A)$ is transitive.

Let A and B be sets with $B \subseteq A$. Determine if the following are true or false.

82. $A \cap B = A$

False. Let $A = \{0, 1\}$ and $B = \{1\}$. Then $A \cap B = \{1\} \neq A$.

83. $A \setminus B \subseteq A$

True. Let $x \in A \setminus B$. Then $x \in A$ and $x \notin B$. In particular, $x \in A$. Since $x \in A \setminus B$ was arbitrary, $A \setminus B \subseteq A$.

84. $B \in \mathcal{P}(A)$

True. This follows from the definition of $\mathcal{P}(A)$.

85. $B \subseteq \mathcal{P}(A)$

False. Let $A = \{a, b\}$ and $B = \{a\}$. Then $\mathcal{P}(A) = \{\emptyset, \{a\}, \{b\}, \{a, b\}\}$. Now, $a \in B$, but $a \notin \mathcal{P}(A)$. Therefore, $B \nsubseteq \mathcal{P}(A)$.

86. $\mathcal{P}(B) \in \mathcal{P}(A)$

False. Let $A = \{0, 1\}$ and $B = \{1\}$. Then $\mathcal{P}(A) = \{\emptyset, \{0\}, \{1\}, \{0, 1\}\}$ and $\mathcal{P}(B) = \{\emptyset, \{1\}\} \notin \mathcal{P}(A)$.

87. $\mathcal{P}(B) \subseteq \mathcal{P}(A)$

True. Let A and B be sets with $B \subseteq A$ and let $X \in \mathcal{P}(B)$. Then $X \subseteq B$ Since $X \subseteq B$ and $B \subseteq A$, by the transitivity of $\subseteq$, $X \subseteq A$. So, $X \in \mathcal{P}(A)$. Since $X \in \mathcal{P}(B)$ was arbitrary, $\mathcal{P}(B) \subseteq \mathcal{P}(A)$.

LEVEL 1

I ⋆	a	b
a	a	a
b	a	a

II ⋆	a	b
a	a	b
b	c	a

III ⋆	a	b
a	a	b
b	b	a

IV ⋆	a	b
a	a	a
b	b	b

For each of the multiplication tables defined on the set $S = \{a, b\}$ above, determine if each of the following is true or false:

1. ⋆ defines a binary operation on S.

For tables I, III, and IV, ⋆ **does** define a binary operation because only a and b appear inside each of these tables. For table II, ⋆ does **not** define a binary operation because an element different from a and b appears in the table (assuming that $c \neq a$ and $c \neq b$).

2. ⋆ is commutative in S.

Since there are just two elements a and b, we need only check if a and b commute ($a \star b = b \star a$). This is very easy to see just by looking at the tables. We simply check if the entries on opposite sides of the main diagonal are the same.

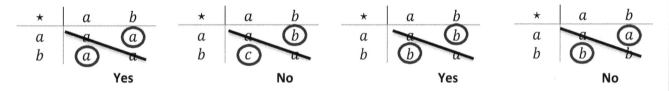

| | Yes | | No | | Yes | | No |

We see that for tables I and III, ⋆ **is** commutative for S, whereas for tables II and IV, ⋆ **is not** commutative for S.

3. a is an identity with respect to ⋆.

To see if a is an identity with respect to ⋆, we need to check if $a \star a = a$, $a \star b = b$, and $b \star a = b$. This is also very easy to see just by looking at the tables. We simply check if the row corresponding to a is the same as the "input row," and if the column corresponding to a is the same as the "input column."

⋆	a	b
a	a	a
b	a	a

No

⋆	a	b
a	a	b
b	c	a

Maybe

⋆	a	b
a	a	b
b	b	a

Maybe

⋆	a	b
a	a	a
b	b	b

No

We see that for tables I and IV, the row corresponding to a is **not** the same as the "input row." So, for I and IV, a is **not** an identity with respect to ⋆.

We still need to check the columns for tables II and III.

$\star$	a	b
a	a	b
b	c	a

No

$\star$	a	b
a	a	b
b	b	a

Yes

We see that for table II, the column corresponding to a is **not** the same as the "input column." So, for II, a is **not** an identity with respect to $\star$.

For table III, a **is** an identity with respect to $\star$.

4. b is an identity with respect to $\star$.

To see if b is an identity with respect to $\star$, we need to check if $a \star b = a$, $b \star a = a$, and $b \star b = b$. Again, this is very easy to see just by looking at the tables. In this case, we see that for each table, the row corresponding to b is **not** the same as the "input row."

$\star$	a	b
a	a	a
b	a	a

No

$\star$	a	b
a	a	b
b	c	a

No

$\star$	a	b
a	a	b
b	b	a

No

$\star$	a	b
a	a	a
b	b	b

No

So, b is **not** an identity with respect to $\star$ in all four cases.

Notes on Problems 1 through 4: (1) Table I defines a semigroup $(S,\star)$. To see that $\star$ is associative in S, just observe that all the outputs are the same. Therefore, there cannot be a counterexample to associativity. For example, $(a \star b) \star b = a \star b = a$ and $a \star (b \star b) = a \star a = a$.

(2) Table I does **not** define a monoid. Problems 3 and 4 showed us that there is no identity with respect to $\star$.

(3) Table III defines a commutative group $(S,\star)$ with identity a. a and b are each their own inverses because $a \star a = a$ and $b \star b = a$ (remember that a is the identity). Associativity can be checked by brute force. There are eight instances that need to be verified. For example, $(a \star a) \star b = a \star b = b$ and $a \star (a \star b) = a \star b = b$. So, $(a \star a) \star b = a \star (a \star b)$. If you do it this way, make sure you check the other seven instances. Alternatively, we can observe that the multiplication table is identical to the multiplication table for $(C_2, +)$ if we replace a with 0 and b with 1.

$\star$	0	1
0	0	1
1	1	0

(4) Table IV defines a semigroup $(S,\star)$ known as the **left zero semigroup**. The name of this semigroup comes from the fact that $a \star a = a$ and $a \star b = a$, so that a is behaving just like 0 behaves when multiplying on the left (0 times anything equals 0). Notice that $b \star a = b \neq a$, so that a does **not** behave like 0 when multiplying on the right. Similar computations show that b also behaves like 0 from the left. The dedicated reader may want to check associativity by brute force, as described in Note 3.

(5) Table IV does **not** define a monoid. Problems 3 and 4 showed us that there is no identity with respect to $\star$.

28

∘	a	b	c	d
a	a	a	a	b
b	d	d	b	b
c	a	b	c	d
d	c	c	d	d

The multiplication table above is defined on the set $S = \{a, b, c, d\}$.

5. Is S closed under $\circ$?

Yes. Only a, b, c, and d appear inside the table.

6. Compute $a \circ b$.

$a \circ b = \boldsymbol{a}$.

∘	a	b	c	d
a	a	a	a	b
b	d	d	b	b
c	a	b	c	d
d	c	c	d	d

7. Is $\circ$ commutative in S? Why or why not?

No. For example, $a \circ b = a$, whereas $b \circ a = d$. So, $a \circ b \neq b \circ a$.

∘	a	b	c	d
a	a	a	a	b
b	d	d	b	b
c	a	b	c	d
d	c	c	d	d

8. Is $\circ$ associative in S? Why or why not?

No. For example, $(b \circ d) \circ b = b \circ b = d$, whereas $b \circ (d \circ b) = b \circ c = b$. Therefore, we see that $(b \circ d) \circ b \neq b \circ (d \circ b)$.

9. Does S have an identity with respect to $\circ$? If so, what is it?

Yes. The identity is c

∘	a	b	c	d
a	a	a	a	b
b	d	d	b	b
c	a	b	c	d
d	c	c	d	d

∘	a	b	c	d
a	a	a	a	b
b	d	d	b	b
c	a	b	c	d
d	c	c	d	d

Let $S = \{e, a\}$.

10. Show that there are exactly two monoids on S with identity e.

Since $e \star x = x \star e = x$ for all x in the monoid, we can easily fill out the first row and the first column of the table.

$\star$	e	a
e	e	a
a	a	$\boxdot$

The entry labeled with $\boxdot$ must be either e or a because we need $\star$ to be a binary operation on S.

Case 1: If we let $\boxdot$ be a, we get the following table.

$\star$	e	a
e	e	a
a	a	a

Associativity holds because any computation of the form $(x \star y) \star z$ or $x \star (y \star z)$ will result in a if any of x, y, or z is a. So, all that is left to check is that $(e \star e) \star e = e \star (e \star e)$. But each side of that equation is equal to e.

So, with this multiplication table, $(S, \star)$ **is** a monoid.

Case 2: If we let $\boxdot$ be e, we get the following table.

$\star$	e	a
e	e	a
a	a	e

Let's check that associativity holds. There are eight instances to check.

$$(e \star e) \star e = e \star e = e \qquad e \star (e \star e) = e \star e = e$$
$$(e \star e) \star a = e \star a = a \qquad e \star (e \star a) = e \star a = a$$
$$(e \star a) \star e = a \star e = a \qquad e \star (a \star e) = e \star a = a$$
$$(a \star e) \star e = a \star e = a \qquad a \star (e \star e) = a \star e = a$$
$$(e \star a) \star a = a \star a = e \qquad e \star (a \star a) = e \star e = e$$
$$(a \star e) \star a = a \star a = e \qquad a \star (e \star a) = a \star a = e$$
$$(a \star a) \star e = e \star e = e \qquad a \star (a \star e) = a \star a = e$$
$$(a \star a) \star a = e \star a = a \qquad a \star (a \star a) = e \star a = a$$

So, with this multiplication table, $(S, \star)$ **is** a monoid.

11. Determine if either of the two monoids on S is a group.

This first monoid is **not** a group because a has no inverse. Indeed, $a \star e = a \neq e$ and $a \star a = a \neq e$.

The second monoid **is** a group. Since $e \star e = e$, e is its own inverse. Since $a \star a = e$, a is also its own inverse.

12. Are either of the monoids on S commutative?

This first monoid is commutative because $a \star e = a$ and $e \star a = a$.

This second monoid is also commutative for the same reason.

LEVEL 2

Define $\star$ on $\mathbb{N}$ by $a \star b = b$.

13. Is $\star$ a binary operation on $\mathbb{N}$?

Yes. The output is always b.

14. Is $\star$ commutative in $\mathbb{N}$?

No. For example, $2 \star 3 = 3$, whereas $3 \star 2 = 2$.

15. Is $\star$ associative in $\mathbb{N}$?

Yes. $(a \star b) \star c = c = b \star c = a \star (b \star c)$.

16. Does $\mathbb{N}$ have an identity with respect to $\star$? If so, what is it?

No. Let $a \in \mathbb{N}$. Then $(a + 1) \star a = a \neq a + 1$. So, a is not an identity. Since a was an arbitrary element of $\mathbb{N}$, we showed that there is no identity.

17. Is $(\mathbb{N}, \star)$ a semigroup?

Yes by Problem 13 and Problem 15.

18. Is $(\mathbb{N}, \star)$ a monoid?

No by Problem 16.

+	0	1		·	0	1
0	0	1		0	1	0
1	1	0		1	0	1

The addition and multiplication tables above are defined on the set $S = \{0, 1\}$.

19. Does $+$ define a binary operation on S?

Yes because only 0 and 1 appears inside the addition table.

20. Does $\cdot$ define a binary operation on S?

Yes because only 0 and 1 appears inside the multiplication table.

21. Does S have an identity with respect to $+$? If so, what is it?

Yes. The identity is 0.

22. Does S have an identity with respect to $\cdot$? If so, what is it?

Yes. The identity is 1.

23. Is $\cdot$ distributive over $+$ in S?

No. For example, $0(1+1) = 0 \cdot 0 = 1$ and $0 \cdot 1 + 0 \cdot 1 = 0 + 0 = 0$. So, $0(1+1) \neq 0 \cdot 1 + 0 \cdot 1$.

24. Explain why $(S, +, \cdot)$ does **not** define a ring.

Explanation 1: By Problem 23, multiplication is **not** distributive over addition in S, and so, $(S, +, \cdot)$ does not define a ring.

Explanation 2: By Ring Fact 1, if $(S, +, \cdot)$ were a ring, we would have $0 \cdot 0 = 0$. So, $(S, +, \cdot)$ does not define a ring.

+	0	1	2
0	0	1	2
1	1	2	0
2	2	0	1

$\cdot$	0	1	2
0	0	0	0
1	0	1	2
2	0	2	2

The addition and multiplication tables above are defined on the set $S = \{0, 1, 2\}$.

25. Show that $(S, +, \cdot)$ does **not** define a field.

We have $2 \cdot 0 = 0$, $2 \cdot 1 = 2$, and $2 \cdot 2 = 2$. So, 2 has no multiplicative inverse, and therefore, $(S, +, \cdot)$ does **not** define a field.

26. Does $(S, +, \cdot)$ define a ring?

No because distributivity fails. For example, $2(1+1) = 2 \cdot 2 = 2$, whereas $2 \cdot 1 + 2 \cdot 1 = 2 + 2 = 1$.

Let $S = \{0, 1\}$ and suppose that $(S, +, \cdot)$ is a ring with additive identity 0 and multiplicative identity 1.

27. Draw the tables for addition and multiplication.

Since $(S, +)$ is a commutative group, by the solutions to Problems 10 and 11, the addition table must be the following.

+	0	1
0	0	1
1	1	0

Since $(S, \cdot)$ is a monoid and 1 is the multiplicative identity, by the solution to Problem 10, the multiplication table must be one of the following.

·	0	1
0	1	0
1	0	1

·	0	1
0	0	0
1	0	1

However, we showed in Problem 24 that if we use the table on the left, then $(S, +, \cdot)$ will **not** define a ring.

So, the addition and multiplication tables must be as follows:

+	0	1
0	0	1
1	1	0

·	0	1
0	0	0
1	0	1

28. Verify that with the tables you drew in Problem 14 that $(S, +, \cdot)$ is a ring.

Since we already know that $(S, +)$ is a commutative group and $(S, \cdot)$ is a monoid, all we need to verify is that distributivity holds. Since $\cdot$ is commutative for S (by the solution to Problem 12), it suffices to verify left distributivity. We will do this by brute force. There are eight instances to check.

$$0(0 + 0) = 0 \cdot 0 = 0 \qquad 0 \cdot 0 + 0 \cdot 0 = 0 + 0 = 0$$
$$0(0 + 1) = 0 \cdot 1 = 0 \qquad 0 \cdot 0 + 0 \cdot 1 = 0 + 0 = 0$$
$$0(1 + 0) = 0 \cdot 1 = 0 \qquad 0 \cdot 1 + 0 \cdot 0 = 0 + 0 = 0$$
$$0(1 + 1) = 0 \cdot 0 = 0 \qquad 0 \cdot 1 + 0 \cdot 1 = 0 + 0 = 0$$
$$1(0 + 0) = 1 \cdot 0 = 0 \qquad 1 \cdot 0 + 1 \cdot 0 = 0 + 0 = 0$$
$$1(0 + 1) = 1 \cdot 1 = 1 \qquad 1 \cdot 0 + 1 \cdot 1 = 0 + 1 = 1$$
$$1(1 + 0) = 1 \cdot 1 = 1 \qquad 1 \cdot 1 + 1 \cdot 0 = 1 + 0 = 1$$
$$1(1 + 1) = 1 \cdot 0 = 0 \qquad 1 \cdot 1 + 1 \cdot 1 = 1 + 1 = 0$$

So, we see that left distributivity holds, and therefore $(S, +, \cdot)$ is a ring.

29. Is $(S, +, \cdot)$ a field?

Yes. It is easy to see from the multiplication table that multiplication is commutative in S. Also, 1 is invertible with $1^{-1} = 1$. It follows that $(S, +, \cdot)$ is a field.

LEVEL 3

Define $\star$ on $\mathbb{Z}$ by $a \star b = \max\{a, b\}$, where $\max\{a, b\}$ is the largest of a or b.

30. Is $\star$ a binary operation on $\mathbb{Z}$?

Yes. The output is always equal to one of the inputs.

31. Is $\star$ commutative in $\mathbb{Z}$?

Yes. There are two cases to consider:

Case 1 ($a \leq b$): $a \star b = \max\{a, b\} = b = \max\{b, a\} = b \star a$

Case 2 ($b \leq a$): $a \star b = \max\{a, b\} = a = \max\{b, a\} = b \star a$

32. Is $\star$ associative in $\mathbb{Z}$?

Yes. There are 6 cases to consider:

Case 1 ($a \leq b \leq c$):
$$(a \star b) \star c = \max\{a, b\} \star c = b \star c = \max\{b, c\} = c$$
$$a \star (b \star c) = a \star \max\{b, c\} = a \star c = \max\{a, c\} = c$$

Case 2 ($a \leq c \leq b$):
$$(a \star b) \star c = \max\{a, b\} \star c = b \star c = \max\{b, c\} = b$$
$$a \star (b \star c) = a \star \max\{b, c\} = a \star b = \max\{a, b\} = b$$

Case 3 ($b \leq a \leq c$):
$$(a \star b) \star c = \max\{a, b\} \star c = a \star c = \max\{a, c\} = c$$
$$a \star (b \star c) = a \star \max\{b, c\} = a \star c = \max\{a, c\} = c$$

Case 4 ($b \leq c \leq a$):
$$(a \star b) \star c = \max\{a, b\} \star c = a \star c = \max\{a, c\} = a$$
$$a \star (b \star c) = a \star \max\{b, c\} = a \star c = \max\{a, c\} = a$$

Case 5 ($c \leq a \leq b$):
$$(a \star b) \star c = \max\{a, b\} \star c = b \star c = \max\{b, c\} = b$$
$$a \star (b \star c) = a \star \max\{b, c\} = a \star b = \max\{a, b\} = b$$

Case 6 ($c \leq b \leq a$):
$$(a \star b) \star c = \max\{a, b\} \star c = a \star c = \max\{a, c\} = a$$
$$a \star (b \star c) = a \star \max\{b, c\} = a \star b = \max\{a, b\} = a$$

33. Does $\mathbb{Z}$ have an identity with respect to $\star$? If so, what is it?

No. Let $a \in \mathbb{Z}$. Then $(a - 1) \star a = a \neq a - 1$. So, a is not an identity. Since a was an arbitrary element of $\mathbb{Z}$, we showed that there is no identity.

34. Is $(\mathbb{Z}, \star)$ a commutative semigroup?

Yes by Problems 30, 31, and 32.

35. Is $(\mathbb{Z}, \star)$ a commutative monoid?

No by Problem 33.

Let $(G, \star)$ be a group with $G = \{e, a, b, c\}$, where e is the identity. Construct the multiplication table for G under the following conditions:

36. $a^2 = e$ and $b^2 = e$

34

Since $e \star x = x \star e = x$ for all x in the group, we can easily fill out the first row, the first column, and two more entries of the table.

$\star$	e	a	b	c
e	e	a	b	c
a	a	e	$\boxdot$	
b	b	$\boxdot$	e	
c	c			

Each of the entries labeled with $\boxdot$ cannot be a, e, or b (Why?), and so they must be c. So, we get the following:

$\star$	e	a	b	c
e	e	a	b	c
a	a	e	c	b
b	b	c	e	
c	c	b		

The rest of the table is now determined:

$\star$	e	a	b	c
e	e	a	b	c
a	a	e	c	b
b	b	c	e	a
c	c	b	a	e

Note: This table gives a group $(G, \star)$ called the **Klein four group**.

37. $a^2 = b$ and $b^2 = e$

Since $e \star x = x \star e = x$ for all x in the group, we can easily fill out the first row and the first column of the table.

$\star$	e	a	b	c
e	e	a	b	c
a	a			
b	b			
c	c			

We now add in $a \star a = a^2 = b$ and $b \star b = b^2 = e$.

$\star$	e	a	b	c
e	e	a	b	c
a	a	b	$\boxdot$	
b	b		e	
c	c			

Now, the entry labeled with $\boxdot$ cannot be a or b because a and b appear in that row. It also cannot be e because e appears in that column. Therefore, the entry labeled with $\boxdot$ must be c. It follows that the entry to the right of $\boxdot$ must be e, and the entry at the bottom of the column must be a.

$\star$	e	a	b	c
e	e	a	b	c
a	a	b	c	e
b	b	$\odot$	e	a
c	c		a	

Now, the entry labeled with $\odot$ cannot be b or e because b and e appear in that row. It also cannot be a because a appears in that column. Therefore, the entry labeled with $\odot$ must be c. The rest of the table is then determined.

$\star$	e	a	b	c
e	e	a	b	c
a	a	b	c	e
b	b	c	e	a
c	c	e	a	b

Note: Observe that in the table we produced, $b = a \star a = a^2$ and $c = b \star a = a^2 \star a = a^3$. So, another way to draw the table is as follows:

$\star$	e	a	a^2	a^3
e	e	a	a^2	a^3
a	a	a^2	a^3	e
a^2	a^2	a^3	e	a
a^3	a^3	e	a	a^2

This group is the **cyclic group of order 4**.

Let $S = \{-1, 1, -i, i\}$, where i is the complex number such that $i^2 = -1$.

38. Is $+$ a binary operation on S? If so, draw the multiplication table.

No. For example, $1 + 1 = 2 \notin S$.

39. Is $\cdot$ a binary operation on S? If so, draw the multiplication table.

Yes.

$\cdot$	1	-1	i	$-i$
1	1	-1	i	$-i$
-1	-1	1	$-i$	i
i	i	$-i$	-1	1
$-i$	$-i$	i	1	-1

40. Explain why $\cdot$ is associative in S.

$S \subseteq \mathbb{C}$ and $\cdot$ is associative in $\mathbb{C}$.

41. Is $(S, \cdot)$ a group? If so, what is the identity, and what is the inverse of each element in S?

Yes. Identity is 1, $1^{-1} = 1$, $(-1)^{-1} = -1$, $i^{-1} = -i$, $(-i)^{-1} = i$

If $(R, +, \cdot)$ is a ring, then $a \in R$ is called a **zero divisor** if $a \neq 0$ and there is an element $b \in R$ with $b \neq 0$ such that $ab = 0$. Find all zero divisors in each of the following rings.

42. $(C_5, +, \cdot)$

No zero divisors.

43. $(C_6, +, \cdot)$

2 and **3** because $2 \cdot 3 = 0$.

44. $(\mathbb{Z}, +, \cdot)$

No zero divisors.

LEVEL 4

Let $(G, \star)$ be a group with $a, b \in G$, and let a^{-1} and b^{-1} be the inverses of a and b, respectively. Verify each of the following:

45. $(a \star b)^{-1} = b^{-1} \star a^{-1}$.

$$(a \star b) \star (b^{-1} \star a^{-1}) = a \star \left(b \star (b^{-1} \star a^{-1}) \right) = a \star \left((b \star b^{-1}) \star a^{-1} \right) = a \star (e \star a^{-1}) = a \star a^{-1} = e$$

and

$$(b^{-1} \star a^{-1}) \star (a \star b) = b^{-1} \star \left(a^{-1} \star (a \star b) \right) = b^{-1} \star \left((a^{-1} \star a) \star b \right) = b^{-1} \star (e \star b) = b^{-1} \star b = e.$$

So, $(a \star b)^{-1} = (b^{-1} \star a^{-1})$. □

Notes: (1) For the first and second equalities we used the associativity of $\star$ in G.

(2) For the third equality, we used the inverse property of $\star$ in G.

(3) For the fourth equality, we used the identity property of $\star$ in G.

(4) For the last equality, we again used the inverse property of $\star$ in G.

(5) Since multiplying $a \star b$ on either side by $b^{-1} \star a^{-1}$ results in the identity element e, it follows that $b^{-1} \star a^{-1}$ is the inverse of $a \star b$.

(6) In a group, to verify that an element h is the inverse of an element g, it suffices to show that $g \star h = e$ **or** $h \star g = e$ (this is Group Fact 2). In other words, we can show that $g \star h = e \rightarrow h \star g = e$ and we can show that $h \star g = e \rightarrow g \star h = e$.

For example, to see that $g \star h = e \rightarrow h \star g = e$, suppose that $g \star h = e$ and k is the inverse of g. Then $g \star k = k \star g = e$. Since $g \star h = e$ and $g \star k = e$, we have $g \star h = g \star k$. By multiplying by g^{-1} on each side of this equation, and using associativity, the inverse property, and the identity property, we get $h = k$. So, h is in fact the inverse of g.

Showing that $h \star g = e \rightarrow g \star h = e$ is similar. Thus, in the solution above, we need only show one of the sequences of equalities given. The second one follows for free.

46. The inverse of a^{-1} is a.

Since a^{-1} is the inverse of a, we have $a \star a^{-1} = a^{-1} \star a = e$. But this sequence of equations also says that a is the inverse of a^{-1}.

Let $(F, +, \cdot)$ be a field with $\mathbb{N} \subseteq F$.

47. Explain why $\mathbb{Z} \subseteq F$.

Let $n \in \mathbb{Z}$. If $n \in \mathbb{N}$, then $n \in F$ because $\mathbb{N} \subseteq F$. If $n \notin \mathbb{N}$, then $-n \in \mathbb{N}$. So, $-n \in F$. Since F is a field, we have $-(-n) \in F$. By Problem 46 above, $-(-n) = n$. So, $n \in F$. Since n was an arbitrary element of $\mathbb{Z}$, we see that $\mathbb{Z} \subseteq F$.

48. Explain why $\left\{ \frac{1}{n} \mid n \in \mathbb{Z}^* \right\} \subseteq F$.

For each $n \in \mathbb{Z}^*$, $\frac{1}{n} = n^{-1} \in F$ because $n \in F$ and the multiplicative inverse property holds in F. Since n was an arbitrary element of $\mathbb{Z}^*$, we see that $\left\{ \frac{1}{n} \mid n \in \mathbb{Z}^* \right\} \subseteq F$.

49. Explain why $\mathbb{Q} \subseteq F$.

Let $\frac{m}{n} \in \mathbb{Q}$. Then $m \in \mathbb{Z}$ and $n \in \mathbb{Z}^*$. Since $\mathbb{Z} \subseteq F$, $m \in F$. Since $n \in \mathbb{Z}^*$, by Problem 48, we have $\frac{1}{n} \in F$. Therefore, $\frac{m}{n} = \frac{m \cdot 1}{1 \cdot n} = \frac{m}{1} \cdot \frac{1}{n} = m\left(\frac{1}{n}\right) \in F$ because F is closed under multiplication. Since $\frac{m}{n}$ was an arbitrary element of $\mathbb{Q}$, we see that $\mathbb{Q} \subseteq F$.

Let $(F, +, \cdot)$ be a field.

50. Show that $\cdot$ is commutative in F.

Let $x, y \in F$. If $x, y \in F^*$, then $xy = yx$. If $x = 0$, then $xy = 0y = 0$ and $yx = y \cdot 0 = 0$ by Ring Fact 1. If $y = 0$, then $xy = x \cdot 0 = 0$ and $yx = 0x = 0$ by Ring Fact 1. In all cases, we have $xy = yx$.

51. Show that $\cdot$ is associative in F.

Let $x, y, z \in F$. We will use Ring Fact 1 several times. If $x, y, z \in F^*$, then $(xy)z = x(yz)$. If $x = 0$, then $(xy)z = (0y)z = 0z = 0$ and $x(yz) = 0(yz) = 0$. If $y = 0$, then $(xy)z = (x \cdot 0)z = 0z = 0$ and $x(yz) = x(0z) = x \cdot 0 = 0$. If $z = 0$, then $(xy)z = (xy) \cdot 0 = 0$ and $x(yz) = x(y \cdot 0) = x \cdot 0 = 0$. In all cases, we have $(xy)z = x(yz)$.

52. Show that 1 is a multiplicative identity in F.

Let $x \in F$. If $x \in F^*$, then $1x = x \cdot 1 = x$. If $x = 0$, then by Ring Fact 1, $1x = 1 \cdot 0 = 0$ and $x \cdot 1 = 0 \cdot 1 = 0$. In all cases, we have $1x = x \cdot 1 = x$.

53. Explain why $(F, \cdot)$ is a commutative monoid.

We first show that $\cdot$ is a binary operation on F.

Let $x, y \in F$. If $x, y \in F^*$, then $xy \in F$ because $\cdot$ is a binary operation on F^*. If $x = 0$, then we have $xy = 0y = 0 \in F$ by Ring Fact 1. If $y = 0$, then $xy = x \cdot 0 = 0 \in F$ by Ring Fact 1. In all cases, we have $xy \in F$. So, $\cdot$ is a binary operation on F.

By Problems 50, 51, and 52, $(F, \cdot)$ is a commutative monoid.

Let $\mathbb{Q}$ be the set of rational numbers.

54. Explain why multiplication is commutative in $\mathbb{Q}$.

Let $\frac{a}{b}, \frac{c}{d} \in \mathbb{Q}$. Then $a, b, c, d \in \mathbb{Z}$ and $b, d \neq 0$. Since multiplication is commutative in $\mathbb{Z}$, we have

$$\frac{a}{b} \cdot \frac{c}{d} = \frac{ac}{bd} = \frac{ca}{db} = \frac{c}{d} \cdot \frac{a}{b}$$

Since $\frac{a}{b}, \frac{c}{d} \in \mathbb{Q}$ were arbitrary, multiplication is commutative in $\mathbb{Q}$.

55. Explain why addition is commutative in $\mathbb{Q}$.

Let $\frac{a}{b}, \frac{c}{d} \in \mathbb{Q}$. Then $a, b, c, d \in \mathbb{Z}$ and $b, d \neq 0$. Since addition and multiplication are commutative in $\mathbb{Z}$,

$$\frac{a}{b} + \frac{c}{d} = \frac{ad + bc}{bd} = \frac{ccb + da}{db} = \frac{c}{d} + \frac{a}{b}$$

Since $\frac{a}{b}, \frac{c}{d} \in \mathbb{Q}$ were arbitrary, addition is commutative in $\mathbb{Q}$.

LEVEL 5

Let $(R, +, \cdot)$ be a ring. Explain why each of the following is true:

56. If $a, b \in R$ with $a + b = b$, then $a = 0$.

$a = a + 0 = a + \big(b + (-b)\big) = (a + b) + (-b) = b + (-b) = 0$.

57. If $a, b \in R$, b^{-1} exists, and $ab = b$, then $a = 1$.

$a = a \cdot 1 = a(bb^{-1}) = (ab)b^{-1} = bb^{-1} = 1$.

58. If $a, b \in R$, a^{-1} exists, and $ab = 1$, then $b = \frac{1}{a}$.

$$b = 1b = (a^{-1}a)b = a^{-1}(ab) = a^{-1} \cdot 1 = a^{-1} = \frac{1}{a}.$$

59. If $a \in R$, then $-a = -1a$.

$-1a + a = -1a + 1a = (-1 + 1)a = 0 \cdot a = 0$ (by Ring Fact 1). So, $-1a$ is the additive inverse of a. Thus, $-1a = -a$.

60. $(-1)(-1) = 1$.

$(-1)(-1) + (-1) = (-1)(-1) + (-1) \cdot 1 = (-1)(-1 + 1) = (-1)(0) = 0$ (by Ring Fact 1). So, $(-1)(-1)$ is the additive inverse of -1. Therefore, $(-1)(-1) = -(-1)$.

Let $(R, +, \cdot)$ be a ring. Recall that $a \in R$ is called a **zero divisor** if $a \neq 0$ and there is an element $b \in R$ with $b \neq 0$ such that $ab = 0$. A commutative ring with no zero divisors is called an **integral domain**.

61. Give an example of an integral domain that is **not** a field.

$(\mathbb{Z}, +, \cdot)$

62. Explain why every field is an integral domain. Are all rings integral domains?

Let F be a field, $a, b \in F$ and $ab = 0$. Assume that $a \neq 0$. Then
$$b = 1b = (a^{-1}a)b = a^{-1}(ab) = a^{-1} \cdot 0.$$

By Ring Fact 1, $a^{-1} \cdot 0 = 0$. So, $b = 0$.

Not all rings are integral domains. $(C_4, +, \cdot)$ is a counterexample (clock arithmetic with a 4-hour clock). Here are the addition and multiplication tables:

+	0	1	2	3
0	0	1	2	3
1	1	2	3	0
2	2	3	0	1
3	3	0	1	2

$\cdot$	0	1	2	3
0	0	0	0	0
1	0	1	2	3
2	0	2	0	2
3	0	3	2	1

Observe that in this ring, $2 \cdot 2 = 0$.

Let $\mathbb{Q}$ be the set of rational numbers.

63. Explain why multiplication is associative in $\mathbb{Q}$.

Let $\frac{a}{b}, \frac{c}{d}, \frac{e}{f} \in \mathbb{Q}$. Then $a, b, c, d, e, f \in \mathbb{Z}$ and $b, d, f \neq 0$. Since multiplication is associative in $\mathbb{Z}$, we have

$$\left(\frac{a}{b} \cdot \frac{c}{d}\right)\frac{e}{f} = \left(\frac{ac}{bd}\right)\frac{e}{f} = \frac{(ac)e}{(bd)f} = \frac{a(ce)}{b(df)} = \frac{a}{b}\left(\frac{ce}{df}\right) = \frac{a}{b}\left(\frac{c}{d} \cdot \frac{e}{f}\right).$$

Since $\frac{a}{b}, \frac{c}{d}, \frac{e}{f} \in \mathbb{Q}$ were arbitrary, multiplication is associative in $\mathbb{Q}$.

64. Explain why addition is associative in $\mathbb{Q}$.

Let $\frac{a}{b}, \frac{c}{d}, \frac{e}{f} \in \mathbb{Q}$. Then $a, b, c, d, e, f \in \mathbb{Z}$ and $b, d, f \neq 0$. Since multiplication and addition are associative in $\mathbb{Z}$, multiplication is (both left and right) distributive over addition in $\mathbb{Z}$, and multiplication is associative in $\mathbb{Z}^*$, we have

$$\left(\frac{a}{b} + \frac{c}{d}\right) + \frac{e}{f} = \frac{ad + bc}{bd} + \frac{e}{f} = \frac{(ad + bc)f + (bd)e}{(bd)f} = \frac{((ad)f + (bc)f) + (bd)e}{(bd)f}$$

$$= \frac{a(df) + (b(cf) + b(de))}{b(df)} = \frac{a(df) + b(cf + de)}{b(df)} = \frac{a}{b} + \frac{cf + de}{df} = \frac{a}{b} + \left(\frac{c}{d} + \frac{e}{f}\right).$$

65. Explain why multiplication is distributive over addition in $\mathbb{Q}$.

Let $\frac{a}{b}, \frac{c}{d}, \frac{e}{f} \in \mathbb{Q}$. Then $a, b, c, d, e, f \in \mathbb{Z}$ and $b, d, f \neq 0$. Let's start with left distributivity.

$$\frac{a}{b}\left(\frac{c}{d} + \frac{e}{f}\right) = \frac{a}{b}\left(\frac{cf + de}{df}\right) = \frac{a(cf + de)}{b(df)}$$

$$\frac{a}{b} \cdot \frac{c}{d} + \frac{a}{b} \cdot \frac{e}{f} = \frac{ac}{bd} + \frac{ae}{bf} = \frac{(ac)(bf) + (bd)(ae)}{(bd)(bf)}$$

We need to verify that $\frac{(ac)(bf) + (bd)(ae)}{(bd)(bf)} = \frac{a(cf + de)}{b(df)}$.

Since $\mathbb{Z}$ is a ring, $(ac)(bf) + (bd)(ae) = bacf + bade = ba(cf + de)$.

Since multiplication is associative and commutative in $\mathbb{Z}$, we have

$$(bd)(bf) = b(d(bf)) = b((db)f) = b((bd)f) = b(b(df)).$$

So, $\frac{(ac)(bf) + (bd)(ae)}{(bd)(bf)} = \frac{ba(cf + de)}{b(b(df))} = \frac{a(cf + de)}{b(df)}$.

For right distributivity, we can use left distributivity together with the commutativity of multiplication in $\mathbb{Q}$.

$$(y + z)x = x(y + z) = xy + xz = yx + zx$$

66. Explain why $(\mathbb{Q}, +, \cdot)$ is a field.

We first check that $(\mathbb{Q}, +)$ is a commutative group.

(Closure) This is Part 1 of Exercise 3.23.

(Associativity) This is Problem 64.

(Identity) This was done in Part 1 of Example 3.22.

(Inverse) This is Part 3 of Exercise 3.23.

(Commutativity) This is Problem 55.

So, $(\mathbb{Q}, +)$ is a commutative group.

We next check that $(\mathbb{Q} \setminus \{0\}, \cdot)$ is a commutative group.

(Closure) This is Part 2 of Exercise 3.23.

(Associativity) This follows from Problem 63 and the fact that associativity is closed downwards.

(Identity) This was done in Part 2 of Example 3.22.

(Inverse) This is Part 4 of Exercise 3.23.

(Commutativity) This follows from Problem 54 and the fact that commutativity is closed downwards.

So, $(\mathbb{Q} \setminus \{0\}, \cdot)$ is a commutative group.

Now we check that multiplication is distributive over addition in $\mathbb{Q}$.

(Distributivity) This is Problem 65.

So, $(\mathbb{Q}, +, \cdot)$ is a field.

Note: There is actually one more issue here. It's not obvious that the definitions of addition and multiplication are even well-defined.

Let's start with multiplication.

Suppose that $\frac{a}{b} = \frac{a'}{b'}$ and $\frac{c}{d} = \frac{c'}{d'}$. We need to check that $\frac{a}{b} \cdot \frac{c}{d} = \frac{a'}{b'} \cdot \frac{c'}{d'}$, or equivalently, $\frac{ac}{bd} = \frac{a'c'}{b'd'}$.

Since $\frac{a}{b} = \frac{a'}{b'}$, we have $ab' = ba'$. Since $\frac{c}{d} = \frac{c'}{d'}$, we have $cd' = dc'$. Now, since $ab' = ba'$, $cd' = dc'$, and multiplication is commutative and associative in $\mathbb{Z}$, we have

$$(ac)(b'd') = (ab')(cd') = (ba')(dc') = (bd)(a'c')$$

Therefore, $\frac{ac}{bd} = \frac{a'c'}{b'd'}$, as desired.

Now let's check that the definition of addition is well-defind.

. Suppose that $\frac{a}{b} = \frac{a'}{b'}$ and $\frac{c}{d} = \frac{c'}{d'}$. We need to check that $\frac{a}{b} + \frac{c}{d} = \frac{a'}{b'} + \frac{c'}{d'}$, or equivalently, $\frac{ad+bc}{bd} = \frac{a'd'+b'c'}{b'd'}$.

Since $\frac{a}{b} = \frac{a'}{b'}$, we have $ab' = ba'$. Since $\frac{c}{d} = \frac{c'}{d'}$, we have $cd' = dc'$. Now, since $ab' = ba'$, $cd' = dc'$, multiplication is commutative and associative in $\mathbb{Z}$, and multiplication is distributive over addition in $\mathbb{Z}$, we have

$$(ad + bc)(b'd') = adb'd' + bcb'd' = ab'dd' + cd'bb' = ba'dd' + dc'bb'$$
$$= bda'd' + bdb'c' = (bd)(a'd' + b'c').$$

Therefore, $\frac{ad+bc}{bd} = \frac{a'd'+b'c'}{b'd'}$, as desired.

Let $\mathbb{C}$ be the set of complex numbers. To answer the following questions, you may use the fact that $(\mathbb{R}, +, \cdot)$ is a field.

67. Explain why $(\mathbb{C}, +)$ is a commutative group.

(Closure) Let $z, w \in \mathbb{C}$. Then there are $a, b, c, d \in \mathbb{R}$ such that $z = a + bi$ and $w = c + di$. By definition, $z + w = (a + bi) + (c + di) = (a + c) + (b + d)i$. Since $\mathbb{R}$ is closed under addition, $a + b \in \mathbb{R}$ and $c + d \in \mathbb{R}$. Therefore, $z + w \in \mathbb{C}$.

(Associativity) Let $z, w, v \in \mathbb{C}$. Then there are $a, b, c, d, e, f \in \mathbb{R}$ such that $z = a + bi$, $w = c + di$, and $v = e + fi$. Since addition is associative in $\mathbb{R}$, we have

$$(z + w) + v = \big((a + bi) + (c + di)\big) + (e + fi) = \big((a + c) + (b + d)i\big) + (e + fi)$$
$$= \big((a + c) + e\big) + \big((b + d) + f\big)i = \big(a + (c + e)\big) + \big(b + (d + f)\big)i$$
$$= (a + bi) + \big((c + e) + (d + f)i\big) = (a + bi) + \big((c + di) + (e + fi)\big) = z + (w + v).$$

(Commutativity) Let $z, w \in \mathbb{C}$. Then there are $a, b, c, d \in \mathbb{R}$ such that $z = a + bi$ and $w = c + di$. Since addition is commutative in $\mathbb{R}$, we have

$$z + w = (a + bi) + (c + di) = (a + c) + (b + d)i = (c + a) + (d + b)i$$
$$= (c + di) + (a + bi) = w + z.$$

(Identity) Let $\overline{0} = 0 + 0i$. We show that $\overline{0}$ is an additive identity for $\mathbb{C}$. Since $0 \in \mathbb{R}$, $\overline{0} \in \mathbb{C}$. Let $z \in \mathbb{C}$. Then there are $a, b \in \mathbb{R}$ such that $z = a + bi$. Since 0 is an additive identity in $\mathbb{R}$, we have

$$\overline{0} + z = (0 + 0i) + (a + bi) = (0 + a) + (0 + b)i = a + bi.$$
$$z + \overline{0} = (a + bi) + (0 + 0i) = (a + 0) + (b + 0)i = a + bi.$$

(Inverse) Let $z \in \mathbb{C}$. Then there are $a, b \in \mathbb{R}$ such that $z = a + bi$. Let $w = -a + (-b)i$. Then

$$z + w = (a + bi) + (-a + (-b)i) = \big(a + (-a)\big) + \big(b + (-b)\big)i = 0 + 0i = \overline{0}.$$
$$w + z = (-a + (-b)i) + (a + bi) = (-a + a) + (-b + b)i = 0 + 0i = \overline{0}.$$

68. Explain why multiplication is associative in $\mathbb{C}$.

Let $z, w, v \in \mathbb{C}$. Then there are $a, b, c, d, e, f \in \mathbb{R}$ such that $z = a + bi$, $w = c + di$, and $v = e + fi$. Since addition and multiplication are associative in $\mathbb{R}$, addition is commutative in $\mathbb{R}$, and multiplication is distributive over addition in $\mathbb{R}$, we have

$$(zw)v = \big((a+bi)(c+di)\big)(e+fi) = \big((ac-bd)+(ad+bc)i\big)(e+fi)$$
$$= [(ac-bd)e-(ad+bc)f]+[(ac-bd)f+(ad+bc)e]i$$
$$= (ace-bde-adf-bcf)+(acf-bdf+ade+bce)i$$
$$= (ace-adf-bcf-bde)+(acf+ade+bce-bdf)i$$
$$= [a(ce-df)-b(cf+de)]+[a(cf+de)+b(ce-df)]i$$
$$= (a+bi)\big((ce-df)+(cf+de)i\big) = (a+bi)\big((c+di)(e+fi)\big) = z(wv).$$

69. Show that $\mathbb{C}$ has the multiplicative inverse property. What is the inverse of the nonzero complex number $a+bi$?

We first show that $\overline{1}=1+0i$ is a multiplicative identity for $\mathbb{C}$. Since $0,1\in\mathbb{R}$, $\overline{1}\in\mathbb{C}^*$. Let $z\in\mathbb{C}$. Then there are $a,b\in\mathbb{R}$ such that $z=a+bi$. Since 0 is an additive identity in $\mathbb{R}$, 1 is a multiplicative identity in $\mathbb{R}$, and $0\cdot x=x\cdot 0=0$ for all $x\in\mathbb{R}$, we have

$$\overline{1}z = (1+0i)(a+bi) = (1a-0b)+(1b+0a)i = 1a+1bi = a+bi.$$

$$z\cdot\overline{1} = (a+bi)(1+0i) = (a\cdot 1-b\cdot 0)+(a\cdot 0+b\cdot 1)i = a\cdot 1+b\cdot 1i = a+bi.$$

Now, let $z\in\mathbb{C}^*$. Then there are $a,b\in\mathbb{R}$ such that $z=a+bi$. Let $w=\frac{a}{a^2+b^2}+\frac{-b}{a^2+b^2}i$. We show that w is the multiplicative inverse of z. We have

$$zw = (a+bi)\left(\frac{a}{a^2+b^2}+\frac{-b}{a^2+b^2}i\right)$$
$$= \left(a\cdot\frac{a}{a^2+b^2}-b\cdot\frac{-b}{a^2+b^2}\right)+\left(a\cdot\frac{-b}{a^2+b^2}+b\cdot\frac{a}{a^2+b^2}\right)i$$
$$= \frac{a^2+b^2}{a^2+b^2}+\frac{-ab+ba}{a^2+b^2}i = 1+0i = \overline{1}.$$
$$wz = \left(\frac{a}{a^2+b^2}+\frac{-b}{a^2+b^2}i\right)(a+bi)$$
$$= \left(\frac{a}{a^2+b^2}\cdot a-\frac{-b}{a^2+b^2}\cdot b\right)+\left(\frac{a}{a^2+b^2}\cdot b+\frac{-b}{a^2+b^2}\cdot a\right)i$$
$$= \frac{a^2+b^2}{a^2+b^2}+\frac{ab-ba}{a^2+b^2}i = 1+0i = \overline{1}.$$

70. Explain why multiplication is distributive over addition in $\mathbb{C}$.

(Left Distributivity) Let $z,w,v\in\mathbb{C}$. Then there are $a,b,c,d,e,f\in\mathbb{R}$ such that $z=a+bi$, $w=c+di$, and $v=e+fi$. Since multiplication is left distributive over addition in $\mathbb{R}$, and addition is associative and commutative in $\mathbb{R}$, we have

$$z(w+v) = (a+bi)[(c+di)+(e+fi)] = (a+bi)[(c+e)+(d+f)i]$$
$$= [a(c+e)-b(d+f)]+[a(d+f)+b(c+e)]i$$
$$= (ac+ae-bd-bf)+(ad+af+bc+be)i$$
$$= [(ac-bd)+(ad+bc)i]+[(ae-bf)+(af+be)i]$$
$$(a+bi)(c+di)+(a+bi)(e+fi) = zw+zv.$$

44

(Right Distributivity) Let $z, w, v \in \mathbb{C}$. There are $a, b, c, d, e, f \in \mathbb{R}$ such that $z = a + bi$, $w = c + di$, and $v = e + fi$. Since multiplication is right distributive over addition in $\mathbb{R}$, and addition is associative and commutative in $\mathbb{R}$, we have

$$(w + v)z = [(c + di) + (e + fi)](a + bi) = [(c + e) + (d + f)i](a + bi)$$
$$= [(c + e)a - (d + f)b] + [(c + e)b + (d + f)a]i$$
$$= (ca + ea - db - fb) + (cb + eb + da + fa)i$$
$$= [(ca - db) + (cb + da)i\,] + [(ea - fb) + (eb + fa)i]$$
$$(c + di)(a + bi) + (e + fi)(a + bi) = wz + vz.$$

71. Explain why $(\mathbb{C}, +, \cdot)$ is a field.

$(\mathbb{C}, +)$ is a commutative group by Problem 67.

We next check that $(\mathbb{C}^*, \cdot)$ is a commutative group.

(Closure) Let $z, w \in \mathbb{C}^*$. Then there are $a, b, c, d \in \mathbb{R}$ such that $z = a + bi$ and $w = c + di$. By definition, $zw = (a + bi)(c + di) = (ac - bd) + (ad + bc)i$. Since $\mathbb{R}$ is closed under multiplication, we have $ac, bd, ad, bc \in \mathbb{R}$. Also, $-bd$ is the additive inverse of bd in $\mathbb{R}$. Since $\mathbb{R}$ is closed under addition, we have $ac - bd = ac + (-bd) \in \mathbb{R}$ and $ad + bc \in \mathbb{R}$. Therefore, $zw \in \mathbb{C}$.

We still need to show that $zw \neq 0$. If $zw = 0$, then $ac - bd = 0$ and $ad + bc = 0$. So, $ac = bd$ and $ad = -bc$. Multiplying each side of the last equation by c gives us $acd = -bc^2$. Replacing ac with bd on the left gives $bd^2 = -bc^2$, or equivalently, $bd^2 + bc^2 = 0$. So, $b(d^2 + c^2) = 0$. If $d^2 + c^2 = 0$, then $c = 0$ and $d = 0$, and so, $w = 0$. If $b = 0$, then $ac = 0$, and so, $a = 0$ or $c = 0$. If $a = 0$, then $z = 0$. If $c = 0$ and $a \neq 0$, then since $ad = -bc = 0$, we have $d = 0$. So, $w = 0$. So, we see that $zw = 0$ implies $z = 0$ or $w = 0$. By contrapositive, since $z, w \in \mathbb{C}^*$, we must have $zw \neq 0$, and so, $zw \in \mathbb{C}^*$.

(Associativity) This follows from Problem 68 and the fact that associativity is closed downwards.

(Commutativity) Let $z, w \in \mathbb{C}^*$. Then there are $a, b, c, d \in \mathbb{R}$ such that $z = a + bi$ and $w = c + di$. Since addition and multiplication are commutative in $\mathbb{R}$, we have

$$zw = (a + bi)(c + di) = (ac - bd) + (ad + bc)i$$
$$= (ca - db) + (cb + da)i = (c + di)(a + bi) = wz$$

(Identity) This is true by Problem 69.

(Inverse) This is also true by Problem 69.

Distributivity is true by Problem 70.

Therefore, $(\mathbb{C}, +, \cdot)$ is field.

Let $S = \{a, b\}$, where $a \neq b$.

72. How many binary operations are there on S?

$2^4 = \mathbf{16}.$

73. Draw the multiplication table for each binary operation on S.

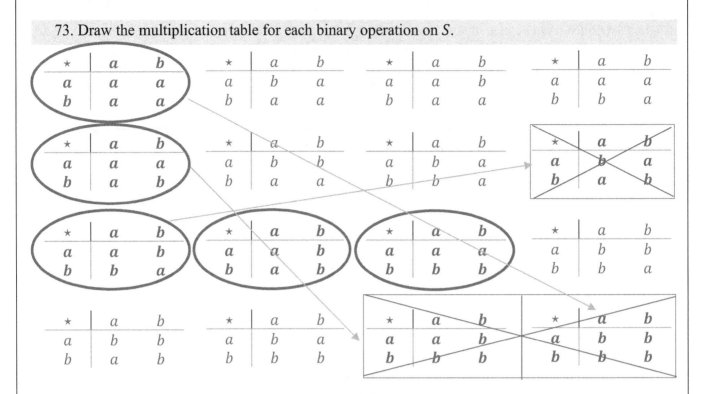

74. How many semigroups are there of the form $(S, \star)$, up to renaming the elements?

Of the 16 binary operations, 8 give rise to semigroups. However, 3 of these are essentially the same as 3 of the others. The 5 circled multiplication tables represent the 5 semigroups. The 3 tables in rectangles that are crossed out also represent semigroups. However, if you interchange the roles of a and b, you'll see that they are the same as 3 of the others with the names changed (arrows are present to indicate the tables that are essentially the same as these). The other 8 tables represent operations that are not associative (the reader should find a counterexample to associativity for each of these). I leave it to the reader to verify that the 5 circled multiplication tables represent semigroups.

Note: A **magma** is a pair $(M, \star)$, where M is a set and $\star$ is a binary operation on M (and no other conditions). In the solution above we showed that there are 16 magmas of the form $(\{a, b\}, \star)$, and of these, 8 are semigroups. However, there are only 5 semigroups up to renaming the elements. Of the 16 magmas, there are only 10 up to renaming the elements. See if you can find the duplicates.

Problem Set 4

LEVEL 1

Write each of the following positive integers as a product of prime factors in canonical form:

1. 16

$16 = 2^4$

2. 19

$19 = 19$

3. 35

$35 = 5 \cdot 7$

4. 105

$105 = 3 \cdot 5 \cdot 7$

5. 275

$275 = 5^2 \cdot 11$

Write each of the following sets using the roster method.

6. $\{n \mid n$ is an even prime number$\}$

$\{2\}$

7. $\{n \mid n$ is a prime number less than 100$\}$

$\{2, 3, 5, 7, 11, 13, 17, 19, 23, 29, 31, 37, 41, 43, 47, 53, 59, 61, 67, 71, 73, 79, 83, 89, 97\}$

8. $\{n \mid n$ is one of the first 25 composite numbers$\}$

$\{4, 6, 8, 9, 10, 12, 14, 15, 16, 18, 20, 21, 22, 24, 25, 26, 27, 28, 30, 32, 33, 34, 35, 36, 38\}$

Find the gcd and lcm of each of the following sets of numbers:

9. $\{6, 9\}$

$\gcd(6, 9) = \mathbf{3}; \operatorname{lcm}(4, 6) = \mathbf{12}.$

10. $\{12, 180\}$

$12 | 180.$ So, $\gcd(12, 180) = \mathbf{12}; \operatorname{lcm}(12, 180) = \mathbf{180}.$

11. $\{2, 3, 5\}$

$\gcd(2, 3, 5) = \mathbf{1}$; $\text{lcm}(2, 3, 5) = \mathbf{30}$.

For each of the integers a and k given, find a number b that shows that a is divisible by k.

12. $a = 8, k = 2$

$8 = 2 \cdot 4$. So, $\boldsymbol{b = 4}$.

13. $a = 30, k = 3$

$30 = 3 \cdot 10$. So, $\boldsymbol{b = 10}$.

14. $a = 17, k = 17$

$17 = 17 \cdot 1$. So, $\boldsymbol{b = 1}$.

15. $a = 1006, k = 1$

$1006 = 1 \cdot 1006$. So, $\boldsymbol{b = 1006}$.

LEVEL 2

Write each of the following positive integers as a product of prime factors in canonical form:

16. 693

$693 = 3^2 \cdot 7 \cdot 11$

17. 67,500

$67,500 = 2^2 \cdot 3^3 \cdot 5^4$

18. 384,659

$384,659 = 11^3 \cdot 17^2$

19. 9,699,690

$9,699,690 = 2 \cdot 3 \cdot 5 \cdot 7 \cdot 11 \cdot 13 \cdot 17 \cdot 19$

Determine if each of the following positive integers is prime:

20. 20

$20 = 2 \cdot 10$. So, 20 is **not prime**.

21. 53

$\sqrt{53} < 8$ and 53 is not divisible by 2, 3, 5, and 7. So, 53 is **prime**.

22. 71

$\sqrt{71} < 9$ and 71 is not divisible by 2, 3, 5, and 7. So, 71 is **prime**.

23. 81

$81 = 9 \cdot 9$. So, 81 is **not prime**.

24. 85

$85 = 5 \cdot 17$. So, 85 is **not prime**.

25. 97

$\sqrt{97} < 10$ and 97 is not divisible by 2, 3, 5, and 7. So, 97 is **prime**.

For $n \in \mathbb{Z}^+$, let $M_n = n! + 1$. Determine if M_n is prime for each of the following values of n.

26. $n = 3$

$M_3 = 3! + 1 = 6 + 1 = 7$. So, M_3 is prime.

27. $n = 4$

$M_4 = 4! + 1 = 24 + 1 = 25$. Since $5|25$, M_4 is **not** prime.

28. $n = 5$

$M_5 = 5! + 1 = 120 + 1 = 121$. Since $11|121$, M_5 is **not** prime.

29. $n = 6$

$M_6 = 6! + 1 = 721$. Since $7|721$, M_6 is **not** prime.

30. $n = 7$

$M_7 = 7! + 1 = 5040 + 1 = 5041$. Since $71|5041$, M_7 is **not** prime

Find the gcd and lcm of each of the following sets of numbers:

31. $\{14, 21, 77\}$

$\gcd(14, 21, 77) = \mathbf{7}$; $\operatorname{lcm}(14, 21, 77) = 2 \cdot 7 \cdot 3 \cdot 11 = \mathbf{462}$.

32. $\{720, 2448, 5400\}$

$720 = 2^4 \cdot 3^2 \cdot 5, \, 2448 = 2^4 \cdot 3^2 \cdot 17, \, 5400 = 2^3 \cdot 3^3 \cdot 5^2.$

$\gcd(720, 2448, 5400) = 2^3 \cdot 3^2 = \mathbf{72}.$

$\text{lcm}(720, 2448, 5400) = 2^4 \cdot 3^3 \cdot 5^2 \cdot 17 = \mathbf{183,600}.$

33. $\{2^{17} \cdot 5^4 \cdot 11^9 \cdot 23, 2^5 \cdot 3^2 \cdot 7^4 \cdot 11^3 \cdot 13\}$

$\gcd(2^{17} \cdot 5^4 \cdot 11^9 \cdot 23, 2^5 \cdot 3^2 \cdot 7^4 \cdot 11^3 \cdot 13) = 2^5 \cdot 11^3.$

$\text{lcm}(2^{17} \cdot 5^4 \cdot 11^9 \cdot 23, 2^5 \cdot 3^2 \cdot 7^4 \cdot 11^3 \cdot 13) = 2^{17} \cdot 3^2 \cdot 5^4 \cdot 7^4 \cdot 11^9 \cdot 13 \cdot 23.$

LEVEL 3

Determine if each of the following numbers is prime:

34. 101

$\sqrt{101} < 11$ and 101 is not divisible by 2, 3, 5, and 7. So, 101 is **prime**.

35. 399

$399 = 7 \cdot 57$. So, 399 is **not prime**.

36. 1829

$1829 = 31 \cdot 59$. So, 1829 is **not prime**.

37. 1933

$\sqrt{1933} < 44$ and 1933 is not divisible by 2, 3, 5, 7, 11, 13, 17, 19, 23, 29, 31, 37, 41, and 43. So, 1933 is **prime**.

38. 8051

$8051 = 83 \cdot 97$. So, 8051 is **not prime**.

39. 13,873

13,873 is **prime** (check that 13,873 is not divisible by any prime number less than 117).

40. 65,623

$65,623 = 137 \cdot 479$. So, 65,623 is **not prime**.

Use the Division Algorithm to find the quotient and remainder when

41. 28 is divided by 3.

$28 = 3 \cdot 9 + 1$. So, **the quotient is 9 and the remainder is 1**.

42. 522 is divided by 6.

$522 = 6 \cdot 87$. So, **the quotient is 87 and the remainder is 0**.

43. 723 is divided by 17.

$723 = 17 \cdot 42 + 9$. So, **the quotient is 42 and the remainder is 9**.

44. 2365 is divided by 71.

$2365 = 71 \cdot 33 + 22$. So, **the quotient is 33 and the remainder is 22**.

Express k as a linear combination of 70 and 100, or explain why it is not possible.

45. $k = 100$

$100 = 0 \cdot 70 + 1 \cdot 100$.

46. $k = 70$

$70 = 1 \cdot 70 + 0 \cdot 100$.

47. $k = 10$

$10 = 3 \cdot 70 - 2 \cdot 100$.

48. $k = 5$

Not possible because $\gcd(70, 100) = 10$ and $5 < 10$.

49. $k = 1$

Not possible because $\gcd(70, 100) = 10$ and $1 < 10$.

For each of the following, use the Euclidean Algorithm to find $\gcd(a, b)$.

50. $a = 15, b = 40$

$$40 = 15 \cdot 2 + 10$$
$$15 = 10 \cdot 1 + 5$$
$$10 = 5 \cdot 2 + 0$$

So, $\gcd(15, 40) = $ **5**.

51. $a = 36, b = 120$

$$120 = 36 \cdot 3 + 12$$
$$36 = 12 \cdot 3 + 0$$

So, $\gcd(36, 120) = \mathbf{12}$.

52. $a = 55, b = 300$

$$300 = 55 \cdot 5 + 25$$
$$55 = 25 \cdot 2 + 5$$
$$25 = 5 \cdot 5 + 0$$

So, $\gcd(55, 300) = \mathbf{5}$.

53. $a = 825, b = 2205$

$$2205 = 825 \cdot 2 + 555$$
$$825 = 555 \cdot 1 + 270$$
$$555 = 270 \cdot 2 + 15$$
$$270 = 15 \cdot 18 + \mathbf{0}$$

So, $\gcd(825, 2205) = \mathbf{15}$.

LEVEL 4

For each of the following, use your computations from Problems 50 through 53 to express $\gcd(a, b)$ as a linear combination of a and b.

54. $a = 15, b = 40$

$$5 = 15 - 10 \cdot 1 = 15 - (40 - 15 \cdot 2) \cdot 1 = 15 - 40 \cdot 1 + 15 \cdot 2 = \mathbf{3 \cdot 15 - 1 \cdot 40}.$$

55. $a = 36, b = 120$

$$2 = 120 - 36 \cdot 3 = \mathbf{-3 \cdot 36 + 1 \cdot 120}.$$

56. $a = 55, b = 300$

$$5 = 55 - 25 \cdot 2 = 55 - (300 - 55 \cdot 5) \cdot 2 = 55 - 300 \cdot 2 + 55 \cdot 10 = \mathbf{11 \cdot 55 - 2 \cdot 300}.$$

57. $a = 825, b = 2205$

$$15 = 555 - 270 \cdot 2 = 555 - (825 - 555 \cdot 1) \cdot 2 = 3 \cdot 555 - 2 \cdot 825$$
$$= 3(2205 - 825 \cdot 2) - 2 \cdot 825 = \mathbf{-8 \cdot 825 + 3 \cdot 2205}.$$

A **prime pair** is a pair of prime numbers of the form $p, p + 2$. For example, $3, 5$ is a prime pair.

58. Is $5, 7$ a prime pair?

Yes.

59. Is $17, 19$ a prime pair?

Yes.

60. Is $1001, 1003$ a prime pair?

No. $1001 = 7 \cdot 11 \cdot 13$

61. Find a prime pair $p, p + 2$ such that $p > 2000$.

$2027, 2029$

Determine how many factors each of the following positive integers has.

62. 50

$50 = 2 \cdot 5^2$. So, the number of factors is $2 \cdot 3 = \textbf{6.}$

Notes: (1) When choosing a factor, we first choose either 2^0 or 2^1 (two choices). We then choose $5^0, 5^1,$ or 5^2 (three choices).

(2) The complete list of factors of 50 is $1, 2, 5, 10, 25, 50$.

63. 1000

$1000 = 2^3 \cdot 5^3$. So, the number of factors is $4 \cdot 4 = \textbf{16.}$

64. $7!$

$7! = 1 \cdot 2 \cdot 3 \cdot 4 \cdot 5 \cdot 6 \cdot 7 = 2^4 \cdot 3^2 \cdot 5 \cdot 7$. So, the number of factors is $5 \cdot 3 \cdot 2 \cdot 2 = \textbf{60.}$

65. $12!$

$12! = 1 \cdot 2 \cdot 3 \cdot 4 \cdot 5 \cdot 6 \cdot 7 \cdot 8 \cdot 9 \cdot 10 \cdot 11 \cdot 12 = 2^{10} \cdot 3^5 \cdot 5^2 \cdot 7 \cdot 11$. So, the number of factors is $11 \cdot 6 \cdot 3 \cdot 2 \cdot 2 = \textbf{792.}$

LEVEL 5

Verify each of the following:

66. If $a, b, c \in \mathbb{Z}$ with $a|b$ and $b|c$, then $a|c$.

Let $a, b, c \in \mathbb{Z}$ with $a|b$ and $b|c$. Since $a|b$, there is $j \in \mathbb{Z}$ such that $b = aj$. Since $b|c$, there is $k \in \mathbb{Z}$ such that $c = bk$. It follows that $c = bk = (aj)k = a(jk)$ because multiplication is associative in $\mathbb{Z}$. Since $j, k \in \mathbb{Z}$ and $\mathbb{Z}$ is closed under multiplication, $jk \in \mathbb{Z}$. Therefore, $a|c$.

67. $\gcd(a, b) \cdot \text{lcm}(a, b) = ab$.

Let $a = p_0^{a_0} p_1^{a_1} \cdots p_n^{a_n}$ and $b = p_0^{b_0} p_1^{b_1} \cdots p_n^{b_n}$ be complete prime factorizations of a and b. Then

$$\gcd(a, b) \cdot \mathrm{lcm}(a, b)$$

$$= p_0^{\min\{a_0, b_0\}} p_1^{\min\{a_1, b_1\}} \cdots p_n^{\min\{a_n, b_n\}} \cdot p_0^{\max\{a_0, b_0\}} p_1^{\max\{a_1, b_1\}} \cdots p_n^{\max\{a_n, b_n\}}$$

$$= p_0^{\min\{a_0, b_0\}} p_0^{\max\{a_0, b_0\}} p_1^{\min\{a_1, b_1\}} p_1^{\max\{a_1, b_1\}} \cdots p_n^{\min\{a_n, b_n\}} p_n^{\max\{a_n, b_n\}}$$

$$= p_0^{\min\{a_0, b_0\} + \max\{a_0, b_0\}} p_1^{\min\{a_1, b_1\} + \max\{a_1, b_1\}} \cdots p_n^{\min\{a_n, b_n\} + \max\{a_n, b_n\}}$$

$$= p_0^{a_0 + b_0} p_1^{a_1 + b_1} \cdots p_n^{a_n + b_n}$$

$$= p_0^{a_0} p_0^{b_0} p_1^{a_1} p_1^{b_1} \cdots p_n^{a_n} p_n^{b_n}$$

$$= p_0^{a_0} p_1^{a_1} \cdots p_n^{a_n} \cdot p_0^{b_0} p_1^{b_1} \cdots p_n^{b_n}$$

$$= ab.$$

68. If $a, b, c, d, e \in \mathbb{Z}$ with $a|b$ and $a|c$, then $a|(db + ec)$.

Let $a, b, c, d, e \in \mathbb{Z}$ with $a|b$ and $a|c$. Since $a|b$, there is $j \in \mathbb{Z}$ such that $b = aj$. Since $a|c$, there is $k \in \mathbb{Z}$ such that $c = ak$. Since $(\mathbb{Z}, +, \cdot)$ is a ring, it follows that

$$db + ec = d(aj) + e(ak) = (da)j + (ea)k = (ad)j + (ae)k = a(dj) + a(ek) = a(dj + ek).$$

Since $\mathbb{Z}$ is closed under multiplication, $dj \in \mathbb{Z}$ and $ek \in \mathbb{Z}$. Since $\mathbb{Z}$ is closed under addition, $dj + ek \in \mathbb{Z}$. So, $a|(db + ec)$.

If $a, b \in \mathbb{Z}^+$ and $\gcd(a, b) = 1$, find each of the following:

69. $\gcd(a, a + 1)$

Since $a + 1 - a = 1$, we see that 1 can be written as a linear combination of a and $a + 1$. Therefore, $\gcd(a, a + 1) = 1$.

70. $\gcd(a, a + 2)$

Since $a + 2 - a = 2$, we see that 2 can be written as a linear combination of a and $a + 2$. Therefore, $\gcd(a, a + 2) \leq 2$. So, $\gcd(a, a + 2) = 1$ or 2.

If a is even, then there is $k \in \mathbb{Z}$ such that $a = 2k$. So, $a + 2 = 2k + 2 = 2(k + 1)$. Thus, we see that $2|a$ and $2|a + 2$. Therefore, if a is even, $\gcd(a, a + 2) = 2$.

If a is odd, then 2 does not divide a. So, $\gcd(a, a + 2)$ cannot be 2, and therefore, must be 1.

71. $\gcd(3a + 2, 5a + 3)$

Since $5(3a + 2) - 3(5a + 3) = 15a + 10 - 15a - 9 = 1$, we see that 1 can be written as a linear combination of $3a + 2$ and $5a + 3$. So, $\gcd(3a + 2, 5a + 3) = 1$.

72. $\gcd(a + b, a - b)$

If d divides $a + b$ and $a - b$, then d divides $(a + b) + (a - b) = 2a$ and d divides $(a + b) - (a - b) = 2b$ because by Problem 68 above, d divides any linear combination of $a + b$ and $a - b$. By Linear Combination Fact 1, $\gcd(2a, 2b)$ can be written as a linear combination of $2a$ and $2b$. So, again by Problem 68, $d | \gcd(2a, 2b) = 2$. So, $d = 1$ or $d = 2$.

If a and b are both odd, then both $a + b$ and $a - b$ are even, and so, $\gcd(a + b, a - b) = 2$.

If a and b do not have the same parity (in other words, one is even and the other is odd), then $a + b$ is odd. So, 2 is not a divisor of $a + b$, and therefore, $\gcd(a + b, a - b) = 1$.

a and b cannot both be even because then $\gcd(a, b) \geq 2$.

Verify each of the following:

73. If n is composite, then n has a prime factor $p \leq \sqrt{n}$ (this is Composite Number Fact 1).

Let n be composite, so that there are integers a, b with $1 < a, b < n$ and $n = ab$. If both a and b are greater than $\sqrt{n}$, then we would have $n = ab > \sqrt{n} \cdot \sqrt{n} = n$, a contradiction. So, either $a \leq \sqrt{n}$ or $b \leq \sqrt{n}$. Without loss of generality, suppose that $a \leq \sqrt{n}$. By Exercise 4.9, a has a prime factor p. Since p is a factor of a and a is a factor n, it follows that p is a factor of n. Also, since p is a factor of a and $a \leq \sqrt{n}$, we have $p \leq \sqrt{n}$.

74. The sum of two odd integers is an even integer.

Let m and n be odd integers. Then there are integers b and c such that $m = 2b + 1$ and $n = 2c + 1$. So, $m + n = (2b + 1) + (2c + 1) = 2b + 2c + 2 = 2(b + c + 1)$ because addition is associative and commutative in $\mathbb{Z}$ and multiplication is distributive over addition in $\mathbb{Z}$. Since $\mathbb{Z}$ is closed under addition, $b + c + 1 \in \mathbb{Z}$. Thus, $m + n$ is even.

75. The product of an even integer and any other integer is an even integer.

Let m be an even integer and let n be any integer. Since m is even, there is an integer b such that $m = 2b$. So, $mn = (2b)n = 2(bn)$ because multiplication is associative in $\mathbb{Z}$. Since $\mathbb{Z}$ is closed under multiplication, $bn \in \mathbb{Z}$. Thus, mn is even.

76. The sum of two integers that are each divisible by k is also divisible by k.

Let m and n be integers that are divisible by k. Then there are integers b and c such that $m = kb$ and $n = kc$. So, $m + n = kb + kc = k(b + c)$ because multiplication is distributive over addition in $\mathbb{Z}$. Since $\mathbb{Z}$ is closed under addition, $b + c \in \mathbb{Z}$. Thus, $m + n$ is divisible by k.

77. The product of an integer divisible by k and any other integer is divisible by k.

Let m be an integer divisible by k and let n be any integer. Since m is divisible by k, there is an integer b such that $m = kb$. So, $mn = (kb)n = k(bn)$ because multiplication is associative in $\mathbb{Z}$. Since $\mathbb{Z}$ is closed under multiplication, $bn \in \mathbb{Z}$. Thus, mn is divisible by k.

78. The product of two odd integers is an odd integer.

Let m and n be odd integers. Then there are integers j and k such that $m = 2j + 1$ and $n = 2k + 1$. So,

$$m \cdot n = (2j + 1) \cdot (2k + 1) = (2j + 1)(2k) + (2j + 1)(1) = (2k)(2j + 1) + (2j + 1)$$
$$= \big((2k)(2j) + 2k\big) + (2j + 1) = \big(2\big(k(2j)\big) + 2k\big) + (2j + 1) = 2(k(2j) + k) + (2j + 1)$$
$$= (2(k(2j) + k) + 2j) + 1 = 2\big((k(2j) + k) + j\big) + 1.$$

Here we used the fact that $(\mathbb{Z}, +, \cdot)$ is a ring. Since $\mathbb{Z}$ is closed under addition and multiplication, we have $(k(2j) + k) + j \in \mathbb{Z}$. Therefore, mn is odd.

Problem Set 5

LEVEL 1

Let S be the set of words in an English dictionary and define a relation $\prec$ on S by $x \prec y$ if x comes before y alphabetically. For example, alligator $\prec$ banana and dragon $\prec$ drainage.

1. Is $\prec$ reflexive on S?

No

2. Is $\prec$ symmetric on S?

No

3. Is $\prec$ transitive on S?

Yes

4. Is $\prec$ antireflexive on S?

Yes

5. Is $\prec$ antisymmetric on S?

Yes (vacuously)

6. Is $\prec$ trichotomous on S?

Yes

7. Does $\prec$ satisfy the comparability condition on S?

No

8. Is $(S, \prec)$ an ordered set?

Yes

Determine if each of the following is an ordered set.

9. $(\mathbb{Z}, >)$

Yes

10. $(\mathbb{Q}, <)$

Yes

11. $(\mathbb{Q}, \leq)$

No

12. $(\mathbb{R}, >)$

Yes

Determine if each of the following sets is bounded or unbounded in $\mathbb{Q}$.

13. $\mathbb{Q}$

Unbounded

14. $\mathbb{Z}^-$

Unbounded

15. $\{5, 10, 15, 20, 25, 30\}$

Bounded

16. $\{1, 2, 3, \ldots, 1000\}$

Bounded

LEVEL 2

Let A be a set with at least two elements and consider the binary relation $\subset$ (proper subset) on $\mathcal{P}(A)$.

17. Is $\subset$ reflexive on $\mathcal{P}(A)$?

No

18. Is $\subset$ symmetric on $\mathcal{P}(A)$?

No

19. Is $\subset$ transitive on $\mathcal{P}(A)$?

Yes

20. Is $\subset$ antireflexive on $\mathcal{P}(A)$?

Yes

21. Is $\subset$ antisymmetric on $\mathcal{P}(A)$?

Yes (vacuously)

22. Is $\subset$ trichotomous on $\mathcal{P}(A)$?

No

23. Does $\subset$ satisfy the comparability condition on $\mathcal{P}(A)$?

No

24. Is $(\mathcal{P}(A), \subset)$ an ordered set?

No

Let a and b be the lengths of the legs of a right triangle and let c be the length of the hypotenuse of the right triangle. Find the third side length of the triangle, given the other two.

25. $a = 9, b = 12$

$c^2 = 9^2 + 12^2 = 81 + 144 = 225$. Therefore, $c = \mathbf{15}$.

26. $a = 40, c = 41$

$41^2 = 40^2 + b^2$. So, $1681 = 1600 + b^2$, and thus, $b^2 = 1681 - 1600 = 81$. Therefore, $\boldsymbol{b = 9}$.

27. $a = 1, b = 2$

$c^2 = 1^2 + 2^2 = 1 + 4 = 5$. Therefore, $\boldsymbol{c = \sqrt{5}}$.

28. $b = 17, c = 26$

$26^2 = a^2 + 17$. So, $676 = a^2 + 289$, and thus, $a^2 = 676 - 289 = 387$. Therefore, we have $\boldsymbol{a = \sqrt{387} = 3\sqrt{43}}$.

For each of the following sets, find the least upper bound in $\mathbb{Q}$ and greatest lower bound in $\mathbb{Q}$ if they exist.

29. $\{x \in \mathbb{Q} \mid -7 \leq x \leq 28\}$

Least upper bound $= \mathbf{28}$

Greatest lower bound $= \mathbf{-7}$

30. $\{x \in \mathbb{Q} \mid x > 15\}$

Least upper bound **does not exist**.

Greatest lower bound $= \mathbf{15}$

31. $\mathbb{Q}^+$

Least upper bound **does not exist**.

Greatest lower bound $= \mathbf{0}$

32. $\{x \in \mathbb{Q} \mid -2 \leq x^2 \leq 2\}$

Least upper bound **does not exist in** $\mathbb{Q}$ (however, in $\mathbb{R}$ it does exist and is equal to $\sqrt{2}$).

Greatest lower bound **does not exist in** $\mathbb{Q}$ (however, in $\mathbb{R}$ it does exist and is equal to $-\sqrt{2}$).

LEVEL 3

In Problems 33 through 36 we will show that there is no smallest positive real number. You may use Ordered Field Fact 2 for these problems. Let $x \in \mathbb{R}$ with $x > 0$.

33. Explain why $\frac{1}{2} > 0$.

Since $2 > 0$, by Ordered Field Fact 2, $\frac{1}{2} > 0$.

34. Explain why $\frac{1}{2}x > 0$.

Since $\frac{1}{2} > 0$ (by Problem 33) and $x > 0$ (given), by property (2) of an ordered field, $\frac{1}{2}x > 0$.

35. Explain why $x > \frac{1}{2}x$.

$x - \frac{1}{2}x = \left(1 - \frac{1}{2}\right)x = \frac{1}{2}x > 0$ by Problem 34. By property (1) of an ordered field, we have

$$x = x - \frac{1}{2}x + \frac{1}{2}x > 0 + \frac{1}{2}x = \frac{1}{2}x.$$

36. Use Problems 33 through 35 to explain why there is no smallest positive real number.

If x is a positive real number, by Problem 34, $\frac{1}{2}x$ is a positive real number, and by Problem 35, $\frac{1}{2}x$ is smaller than x. Since x was an arbitrary positive real number, there is no smallest positive real number.

Let $a, r \in \mathbb{R}$ with $a \geq 0$.

37. Show that if $a = 0$, then a is less than every positive real number.

Let r be a positive real number. By the definition of being positive, $r > 0 = a$. So, $a < 0$. Since r was an arbitrary positive real number, a is less then every positive real number.

38. Show that if $a \neq 0$, then there is a positive real number less than a.

Suppose that $a \neq 0$. Then a is positive. By Problem 36, there is no smallest positive real number. So, there is a positive real number less than a.

39. Explain why $a = 0$ if and only if a is less than every positive real number.

If $a = 0$, then by Problem 37, a is less than every positive real number. If $a \neq 0$, then by Problem 38, there is a positive real number less than a. By contrapositive, if there is no positive real number less than a, then $a = 0$. By the trichotomy of $<$, the statement "there is no positive real number less than a" is equivalent to "a is less than or equal to every positive real number." Now, if a is less than every positive real number, then a is less than or equal to every positive real number. It follows that there is no positive real number less than a, and so, $a = 0$.

In Problems 40 through 42 we will use the Density Property of $\mathbb{R}$ (Real Number Fact 2) to show that given any two distinct real numbers, we can find an irrational number between them. Let $x, y \in \mathbb{R}$.

40. Suppose that $x < y$ and let c be a positive irrational number. Explain why there is a rational number q such that $\frac{x}{c} < q < \frac{y}{c}$.

$\frac{x}{c} < \frac{y}{c}$, and therefore, by the Density Property of $\mathbb{R}$, there is a rational number q such that $\frac{x}{c} < q < \frac{y}{c}$.

41. Suppose that $x < y$ and let c be a positive irrational number. Explain why there is a **nonzero** rational number q such that $\frac{x}{c} < q < \frac{y}{c}$.

By Problem 40, there is a rational number s such that $\frac{x}{c} < s < \frac{y}{c}$. If $s \neq 0$, let $q = s$. If $s = 0$, then we apply the Density Property of $\mathbb{R}$ to get a rational number q such that $\frac{x}{c} < q < 0$.

42. Suppose that $x < y$. Explain why there is an irrational number t such that $x < t < y$.

By Problem 41, there is a nonzero rational number q such that $\frac{x}{c} < q < \frac{y}{c}$. So, $x < cq < y$. If cq were equal to a rational number s, then $c = c \cdot 1 = c \left(q \cdot \frac{1}{q} \right) = (cq) \left(\frac{1}{q} \right) = s \left(\frac{1}{q} \right)$. Since $\mathbb{Q}$ is closed under multiplicative inverses and multiplication, c would be rational, contrary to our assumption that c is irrational. So, $t = cq$ is irrational and $x < t < y$.

LEVEL 4

In Problems 43 through 46 we will use the Completeness Property of $\mathbb{R}$ to show that every nonempty set of real numbers that is bounded below has a greatest lower bound in $\mathbb{R}$. Let S be a nonempty set of real numbers that is bounded below and let $T = \{-x \mid x \in S\}$.

43. Let K be a lower bound for S. Explain why $-K$ is an upper bound for the set T.

Let $y \in T$. Then there is $x \in S$ with $y = -x$. Since $x \in S$, $x \geq K$. So, $y = -x \leq -K$ (**Check this!**). Since $y \in T$ was arbitrary, we have shown that $-K$ is an upper bound for the set T.

44. Explain why T has a least upper bound M.

By Problem 43, T is bounded above. So, by the Completeness Property of $\mathbb{R}$, T has a least upper bound M.

45. Let M be the least upper bound of T. Explain why $-M$ is a lower bound of S.

Let $x \in S$. Then $-x \in T$. Since M is an upper bound for T, $-x \leq M$. So, $x \geq -M$ (**Check this!**). Since $x \in S$ was arbitrary, $-M$ is a lower bound of S.

46. Let M be the least upper bound of T. Explain why $-M$ is a greatest lower bound of S.

By Problem 45, $-M$ is a lower bound of S.

Let $B > -M$. Then $-B < M$ (**Check this!**). Since M is the least upper bound for T, there is $y \in T$ with $y > -B$. So, $-y < B$ (**Check this!**). Since $y \in T$, $-y \in S$. Thus, B is not a lower bound of S.

Therefore, $-M$ is a greatest lower bound of S.

In Problems 47 through 50 we will show that $\mathbb{Q}$ has the Archimedean Property. Let $\frac{a}{b}$ be a positive rational number.

47. Show that $(a+1) - \frac{a}{b} = \frac{a(b-1)+b}{b}$.

$$(a+1) - \frac{a}{b} = \frac{(a+1)}{1} + \left(\frac{-a}{b}\right) = \frac{(a+1)b + 1\cdot(-a)}{1b} = \frac{ab+b-a}{b} = \frac{a(b-1)+b}{b}$$

48. Explain why $(a+1) - \frac{a}{b} > 0$.

Since $\frac{a}{b}$ is positive, either $a, b \in \mathbb{Z}^+$ or $a, b \in \mathbb{Z}^-$. If $a, b \in \mathbb{Z}^+$, then $b - 1 \geq 0$. So, $a(b-1) \geq 0$. Therefore, $a(b-1) + b \geq 0 + b > 0$. Thus, $(a+1) - \frac{a}{b} = \frac{a(b-1)+b}{b} > 0$. If $a, b \in \mathbb{Z}^-$, then $b - 1 < 0$. So, $a(b-1) < 0$. Therefore, $a(b-1) + b < 0$. Thus, $(a+1) - \frac{a}{b} = \frac{a(b-1)+b}{b} > 0$ (since the numerator and denominator are both negative).

49. Explain why $a + 1 > \frac{a}{b}$.

By Problem 48, we have $(a+1) - \frac{a}{b} > 0$. By property (1) of an ordered field,

$$a + 1 = a + 1 - \frac{a}{b} + \frac{a}{b} > 0 + \frac{a}{b} = \frac{a}{b}.$$

50. Use Problems 47 through 49 to explain why $\mathbb{Q}$ has the Archimedean Property.

Let $\frac{a}{b}$ be a rational number. If $\frac{a}{b} \leq 0$, then $\frac{a}{b} < 1$. Otherwise $\frac{a}{b} > 0$, and so, by Problem 49, $a + 1 > \frac{a}{b}$. Since $a, 1 \in \mathbb{Z}$, we have $a + 1 \in \mathbb{Z}$. If $a + 1 \notin \mathbb{N}$, then $\frac{a}{b} < a + 1 < 1$. Otherwise, $a + 1$ is a anatural number greater than $\frac{a}{b}$. So, in all cases, we have found a natural number greater than $\frac{a}{b}$. Since $\frac{a}{b}$ was an arbitrary rational number, $\mathbb{Q}$ has the Archimedean Property.

In Problems 51 through 54 we will show that $\mathbb{R}$ has the Archimedean Property.

51. Suppose that $\mathbb{N}$ is bounded from above in $\mathbb{R}$. Explain why this implies that $\mathbb{N}$ has a least upper bound in $\mathbb{R}$.

This follows from the Completeness Property of $\mathbb{R}$.

52. Let x be the least upper bound of $\mathbb{N}$ in $\mathbb{R}$ (assuming it exists). Explain why $x - 1$ is **not** an upper bound for $\mathbb{N}$.

This is simply because $x - 1 < x$.

53. Assuming that $x - 1$ is not an upper bound for $\mathbb{N}$, show that x is not an upper bound for $\mathbb{N}$.

Since $x - 1$ is **not** an upper bound for $\mathbb{N}$, there is $n \in \mathbb{N}$ such that $x - 1 < n$. Then we have $x = x + (-1 + 1) = (x - 1) + 1 < n + 1$. Since $\mathbb{N}$ is closed under addition, $n + 1 \in \mathbb{N}$. So, x is not an upper bound for $\mathbb{N}$.

54. Use Problems 51 through 53 to explain why $\mathbb{R}$ has the Archimedean Property.

If $\mathbb{N}$ were bounded from above, then by Problem 51, $\mathbb{N}$ would have a least upper bound x. By Problem 52, $x - 1$ is **not** an upper bound of $\mathbb{N}$, and so, by Problem 53, x is not an upper bound for $\mathbb{N}$, contrary to our assumption. It follows that $\mathbb{N}$ is not bounded from above. So, for every $x \in \mathbb{R}$, there is $n \in \mathbb{N}$ such that $n > x$. In other words, $\mathbb{R}$ has the Archimedean Property.

In Problems 55 through 60 we will show that there is no rational number q such that $q^2 = 2$.

55. Let a be an integer such that a^2 is even. Explain why a must be even.

If a were odd, then by Problem 78 in Problem Set 4, $a^2 = a \cdot a$ would be odd.

56. Let $\frac{c}{d}$ be a rational number. Explain why there is a rational number $\frac{a}{b}$ such that $\frac{a}{b} = \frac{c}{d}$ and either a is odd or b is odd (or both).

If c is odd or d is odd, let $a = c$ and $b = d$. Otherwise, c and d are both even. So, there are integers j and k such that $c = 2j$ and $d = 2k$. Then $\frac{c}{d} = \frac{2j}{2k} = \frac{j}{k}$ (because $2jk = 2kj$). If j is odd or k is odd, let $j = a$ and $k = b$. Otherwise, repeat this process. After finitely many iterations, we will get a and b with either a odd or b odd, and $\frac{c}{d} = \frac{a}{b}$.

57. Let $\frac{a}{b}$ be a rational number such that $\left(\frac{a}{b}\right)^2 = 2$. Explain why a must be even.

We have $\frac{2}{1} = 2 = \left(\frac{a}{b}\right)^2 = \left(\frac{a}{b}\right)\left(\frac{a}{b}\right) = \frac{a \cdot a}{b \cdot b} = \frac{a^2}{b^2}$. So, $2b^2 = a^2$, or equivalently, $a^2 = 2b^2$. So, a^2 is even. Since a is an integer, by Problem 55, a is even.

58. Let $\frac{a}{b}$ be a rational number such that $\left(\frac{a}{b}\right)^2 = 2$. Explain why b must be even.

By Problem 57 (and its solution above), $a^2 = 2b^2$ and a is even. So, there is an integer k such that $a = 2k$. Replacing a by $2k$ in the equation $a^2 = 2b^2$, we have $(2k)^2 = 2b^2$. So, $(2k)(2k) = 2b^2$, or equivalently, $2\big(k(2k)\big) = 2b^2$. Therefore, $b^2 = k(2k) = 2k^2$, and so, b^2 is even. By Problem 55, b is even.

59. Explain why there cannot exist a rational number $\frac{a}{b}$ such that $\left(\frac{a}{b}\right)^2 = 2$ and either a is odd or b is odd (or both).

Let $\frac{a}{b}$ be a rational number such that $\left(\frac{a}{b}\right)^2 = 2$. By Problem 57, a is even. By Problem 58, b is even

60. Explain why there does not exist a rational number $\frac{a}{b}$ such that $\left(\frac{a}{b}\right)^2 = 2$.

Let $\frac{a}{b}$ be a rational number $\left(\frac{a}{b}\right)^2 = 2$. By Problem 56, we may assume that a is odd or b is odd (or both). By Problem 59, there is no such rational number.

Suppose that $<$ is a strict linear ordering on $\mathbb{C}$ (the field of complex numbers) satisfying properties (1) and (2) of an ordered field.

61. Assume that $i > 0$. Use property (2) of an ordered field to explain why $-1 > 0$.

If $i > 0$, then $-1 = i^2 = i \cdot i > 0$ by property (2) of an ordered field.

62. Assume that $i < 0$. Use property (1) of an ordered field to explain why $-i > 0$.

If $i < 0$, then $0 = i - i = i + (-i) < 0 + (-i) = -i$ by property (i) of an ordered field. Equivalently, we have $-i > 0$.

63. Assume that $-i > 0$. Use property (2) of an ordered field to explain why $-1 > 0$.

$-1 = i^2 = (-1)(-1)i \cdot i = (-1i)(-1i) = (-i)(-i) > 0$ by property (2) of an ordered field. We also used Problems 59 and 60 from Problem Set 3, as well as associativity and commutativity of multiplication in a field.

64. Assume that $-1 > 0$. Use property (1) of an ordered field to explain why $1 < 0$.

If $-1 > 0$, then $0 < -1$, and so, $1 = 1 + 0 < 1 + (-1) = 1 - 1 = 0$.

65. Assume that $-1 > 0$. Use property (2) of an ordered field to explain why $1 > 0$.

$1 = (-1)(-1) > 0$ by property (2) of an ordered field.

66. Use Problems 61 through 65 to explain why there is no way to turn $\mathbb{C}$ into an ordered field.

If $<$ is a strict linear ordering of $\mathbb{C}$, then by Problem 64, $1 < 0$ and by Problem 65, $1 > 0$, or equivalently, $0 < 1$. By the transitivity of $<$, $0 < 0$, contradicting that $<$ is trichotomous (because $0 = 0$ is also true). So, $\mathbb{C}$ cannot be turned into an ordered field.

In Problems 67 through 71 we will verify Ordered Field Fact 2. Let F be an ordered field and let $x \in F$ with $x > 0$.

67. Explain why $\frac{1}{x} = x^{-1}$ exists and is nonzero.

This is because F is a field and $x \neq 0$.

68. Assume that $\frac{1}{x} < 0$. Use property (1) of an ordered field to explain why $-\frac{1}{x} > 0$.

If $\frac{1}{x} < 0$, then $0 = \frac{1}{x} - \frac{1}{x} = \frac{1}{x} + \left(-\frac{1}{x}\right) < 0 + \left(-\frac{1}{x}\right) = -\frac{1}{x}$ by property (i) of an ordered field. Equivalently, we have $-\frac{1}{x} > 0$.

69. Assume that $-\frac{1}{x} > 0$. Use property (2) of an ordered field to explain why $-1 > 0$.

$-1 = -1 \cdot 1 = -1xx^{-1} = x(-1)x^{-1} = x(-x^{-1}) = x\left(-\frac{1}{x}\right) > 0$ by property (2) of an ordered field. We also used Problem 59 from Problem Set 3, as well as associativity and commutativity of multiplication, the multiplicative inverse property, and the multiplicative identity property in a field.

70. Assume that $-1 > 0$. Use property (1) of an ordered field to explain why $1 < 0$.

If $-1 > 0$, then $0 < -1$. So, $1 = 0 + 1 < -1 + 1 = 0$ by property (i) of an ordered field.

71. Use Problems 67 through 70 to explain why $\frac{1}{x} > 0$.

By Problem 67, $\frac{1}{x}$ exists and is nonzero. If $\frac{1}{x} < 0$, then by Problems 68, 69, and 70, $1 < 0$. By Ordered Field Fact 1, $1 = 1 \cdot 1 > 0$, or equivalently, $0 < 1$. By the transitivity of $<$, $0 < 0$, contradicting that $<$ is trichotomous (because $0 = 0$ is also true). So, $\frac{1}{x} \not< 0$. Since $\frac{1}{x} \not< 0$ and $\frac{1}{x} \neq 0$, by the Trichotomy of $<$, we must have $\frac{1}{x} > 0$.

Problem Set 6

LEVEL 1

Determine if each of the following sets is an interval.

1. $A = \{x \in \mathbb{R} \mid 12 \le x \le 15\}$

Yes

2. $B = \{x \in \mathbb{R} \mid x < -103\}$

Yes

3. $C = \{x \in \mathbb{Q} \mid x < -103\}$

No because there are irrational numbers between any two rational numbers.

4. $D = \mathbb{Q}^-$

No because there are irrational numbers between any two rational numbers.

5. $E = \mathbb{R}^+$

Yes

6. $F = \{x \in \mathbb{R} \mid x \ge -16\}$

Yes

7. $G = \{x \in \mathbb{R} \mid 0 \le x < 999\}$

Yes

8. $\mathbb{R} \setminus \{0\}$

No: For example, $-1 < 0 < 1$, $-1, 1 \in \mathbb{R} \setminus \{0\}$, but $0 \notin \mathbb{R} \setminus \{0\}$.

Sketch the graph of each of the following:

9. $\mathbb{R}$

66

10. $\mathbb{R}^+$

11. $\{-1, 1\}$

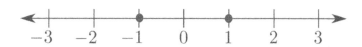

12. $(-1, 1)$

13. $[-1, \infty)$

14. $\mathbb{N}$

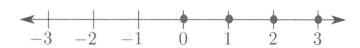

15. $\mathbb{Z}$

16. $(-\infty, -1)$

17. $(1, 2]$

Let $A = (-17, 6)$ and $B = (-1, 17)$. Compute each of the following:

18. $A \cup B$

$(-17, 17)$

19. $A \cap B$

$(-1, 6)$

20. $A \setminus B$

$(-17, -1]$

21. $B \setminus A$

$[6, 17)$

22. $A \, \Delta \, B$

$(-17, -1] \cup [6, 17)$

Let $A = [14, \infty)$ and $B = (-\infty, 15)$. Compute each of the following:

23. $A \cup B$

$(-\infty, \infty)$

24. $A \cap B$

$[14, 15)$

25. $A \setminus B$

$[15, \infty)$

26. $B \setminus A$

$(-\infty, 14)$

27. $A \, \Delta \, B$

$(-\infty, 14) \cup [15, \infty)$

For each of the following, compute $\bigcup X$ and $\bigcap X$.

28. $X = \{\{0, 1, 2\}, \{1, 2, 3\}, \{2, 3, 4\}\}$

$\bigcup X = \{0, 1, 2, 3, 4\}$ $\bigcap X = \{2\}$

29. $X = \{\mathbb{N}, \mathbb{Z}, \mathbb{Q}, \mathbb{R}\}$

$\bigcup X = \mathbb{R}$ $\bigcap X = \mathbb{N}$

30. $X = \{(0, 10), (1, 11), (2, 12), (3, 13), (4, 14)\}$

$\bigcup X = (0, 14)$ $\bigcap X = (4, 10)$

31. $X = \{(-\infty, 20), [-5, 17), (4, 100]\}$

$\bigcup X = (-\infty, 100]$ $\bigcap X = (4, 17)$

32. $X = \{(0, 1], (1, 2], (2, 3], (3, 4]\}$

$\bigcup X = (0, 4]$ $\bigcap X = \emptyset$

Determine if each of the following sets is open, closed, both, or neither.

33. $(5, 11]$

Neither

34. $\{x \in \mathbb{R} \mid x < -103\}$

Open

35. $(12, 17) \cup (26, \infty)$

Open

36. $(0, 5) \cap (2, 6]$

Open: $(0, 5) \cap (2, 6] = (2, 5)$

37. $(0, 5) \cap [2, 6)$

Neither: $(0, 5) \cap [2, 6) = [2, 5)$

38. $(0, 5] \cap [2, \infty)$

Closed: $(0, 5] \cap [2, \infty) = [2, 5]$

39. $(0,1) \cap (1,2)$

Both: $(0,1) \cap (1,2) = \emptyset$

Let S be a set of real numbers. A real number x is called an **accumulation point** of S if every open interval containing x contains at least one point of S different from x. Find the accumulation points of each of the following sets:

40. $\left\{1, \frac{1}{2}, \frac{1}{3}, \dots\right\}$

0

41. $[0,1)$

The set of accumulation points is $[0, 1]$.

42. $\mathbb{Z}$

No accumulation points

43. $\mathbb{Q}$

The set of accumulation points is $\mathbb{R}$.

LEVEL 4

For each of the following, compute $\cup X$ and $\cap X$.

44. $X = \{(0, q] \mid q \in \mathbb{Q}^+\}$

$\cup X = (0, \infty)$ $\cap X = \emptyset$

45. $X = \left\{\left(\frac{1}{n}, 1\right) \mid n \in \mathbb{Z}^+\right\}$

$\cup X = (0, 1)$ $\cap X = \emptyset$

46. $X = \{(n, n+3) \mid n \in \mathbb{Z}\}$

$\cup X = \mathbb{R}$ $\cap X = \emptyset$

47. $X = \left\{\left(0, 1 + \frac{1}{n}\right) \mid n \in \mathbb{Z}^+\right\}$

$\cup X = (0, 2)$ $\cap X = (0, 1]$

48. $X = \left\{\left(-\infty, \frac{1}{n}\right] \mid n \in \mathbb{Z}^+\right\}$

$\cup X = (-\infty, 1]$ $\cap X = (-\infty, 0]$

Determine if each of the following sets is open, closed, both, or neither.

49. $\mathbb{Q}^+$

Neither

50. $\mathbb{Z}$

Closed

51. $\mathbb{R} \setminus \mathbb{N}$

Open

52. $\cup \left\{ \left(0, 1 + \frac{1}{n}\right) \mid n \in \mathbb{Z}^+ \right\}$

Open

53. $\cap \left\{ \left[0, 1 - \frac{1}{n}\right] \mid n \in \mathbb{Z}^+ \right\}$

Closed

If X is a nonempty set of sets, we say that X is **disjoint** if $\cap X = \emptyset$. We say that X is **pairwise disjoint** if for all $A, B \in X$ with $A \neq B$, A and B are disjoint. For each of the following, determine if X is disjoint, pairwise disjoint, both, or neither.

54. $\{(n, n+1) \mid n \in \mathbb{Z}\}$

Both

55. $\{(n, n+1] \mid n \in \mathbb{Z}\}$

Both

56. $\left\{ \left(\frac{1}{n+1}, \frac{1}{n}\right) \mid n \in \mathbb{Z}^+ \right\}$

Both

57. $\{\mathbb{Q}\}$

Neither

58. $\left\{ \mathbb{Q}^-, 2\mathbb{N}, \{n \in \mathbb{N} \mid n \text{ is a prime number greater than 2}\} \right\}$

Both

Let X be a nonempty set of sets. Verify each of the following:

59. For all $A \in X$, $A \subseteq \bigcup X$.

Let $A \in X$ and let $x \in A$. Then there is $B \in X$ such that $x \in B$ (namely A). So, $x \in \bigcup X$. Since x was an arbitrary element of A, we have shown that $A \subseteq \bigcup X$. Since A was an arbitrary element of X, we have shown that for all $A \in X$, we have $A \subseteq \bigcup X$.

60. For all $A \in X$, $\bigcap X \subseteq A$.

Let $A \in X$ and let $x \in \bigcap X$. Then for every $B \in X$, we have $x \in B$. In particular, $x \in A$ (because $A \in X$). Since x was an arbitrary element of $\bigcap X$, we have shown that $\bigcap X \subseteq A$. Since A was an arbitrary element of X, we have shown that for all $A \in X$, we have $\bigcap X \subseteq A$.

Let A be a set and let X be a nonempty set of sets. Verify each of the following:

61. $A \cap \bigcup X = \bigcup\{A \cap B \mid B \in X\}$.

$x \in A \cap \bigcup X \Leftrightarrow x \in A$ and $x \in \bigcup X \Leftrightarrow x \in A$ and there is a $B \in X$ with $x \in B \Leftrightarrow x \in A \cap B$ for some $B \in X \Leftrightarrow x \in \bigcup\{A \cap B \mid B \in X\}$.

62. $A \cup \bigcap X = \bigcap\{A \cup B \mid B \in X\}$.

$x \in A \cup \bigcap X \Leftrightarrow x \in A$ or $x \in \bigcap X \Leftrightarrow x \in A$ or $x \in B$ for every $B \in X \Leftrightarrow x \in A \cup B$ for every $B \in X \Leftrightarrow x \in \bigcap\{A \cup B \mid B \in X\}$.

63. $A \setminus \bigcup X = \bigcap\{A \setminus B \mid B \in X\}$.

$x \in A \setminus \bigcup X \Leftrightarrow x \in A$ and $x \notin \bigcup X \Leftrightarrow x \in A$ and $x \notin B$ for every $B \in X \Leftrightarrow x \in A \setminus B$ for every $B \in X \Leftrightarrow x \in \bigcap\{A \setminus B \mid B \in X\}$.

64. $A \setminus \bigcap X = \bigcup\{A \setminus B \mid B \in X\}$.

$x \in A \setminus \bigcap X \Leftrightarrow x \in A$ and $x \notin \bigcap X \Leftrightarrow x \in A$ and $x \notin B$ for some $B \in X \Leftrightarrow x \in A \setminus B$ for some $B \in X \Leftrightarrow x \in \bigcup\{A \setminus B \mid B \in X\}$.

Verify each of the following:

65. An arbitrary union of open sets in $\mathbb{R}$ is an open set in $\mathbb{R}$.

Let X be a set of open subsets of $\mathbb{R}$ and let $x \in \bigcup X$. Then $x \in A$ for some $A \in X$. Since A is open in $\mathbb{R}$, there is an interval (a, b) with $x \in (a, b)$ and $(a, b) \subseteq A$. By Problem 59 above, we have $A \subseteq \bigcup X$. Since $\subseteq$ is transitive, $(a, b) \subseteq \bigcup X$. Therefore, $\bigcup X$ is open.

66. An arbitrary intersection of closed sets in $\mathbb{R}$ is closed in $\mathbb{R}$.

Let X be a nonempty set of closed subsets of $\mathbb{R}$. Then for each $A \in X$, $\mathbb{R} \setminus A$ is an open set in $\mathbb{R}$. By Problem 65 above, $\cup \{\mathbb{R} \setminus A \mid A \in X\}$ is open in $\mathbb{R}$. Therefore, $\mathbb{R} \setminus \cup \{\mathbb{R} \setminus A \mid A \in X\}$ is closed in $\mathbb{R}$. So, it suffices to show that $\cap X = \mathbb{R} \setminus \cup \{\mathbb{R} \setminus A \mid A \in X\}$. Well, $x \in \cap X$ if and only if for all $A \in X$, $x \in A$ if and only if for all $A \in X$, $x \notin \mathbb{R} \setminus A$ if and only if $x \notin \cup \{\mathbb{R} \setminus A \mid A \in X\}$ if and only if $x \in \mathbb{R} \setminus \cup \{\mathbb{R} \setminus A \mid A \in X\}$. So, $\cap X = \mathbb{R} \setminus \cup \{\mathbb{R} \setminus A \mid A \in X\}$, completing the argument.

Problem Set 7

LEVEL 1

Let $z = 1 + i$ and $w = 2 - 3i$. Compute each of the following:

1. Re z

1

2. Im z

1

3. Re w

2

4. Im w

-3

5. $z + w$

$3 - 2i$

6. $z - w$

$-1 + 4i$

7. $2z$

$2 + 2i$

8. $5w$

$10 - 15i$

9. $2z + 5w$

$12 - 13i$

10. $w - 5z$

$(2 - 3i) - 5(1 + i) = (2 - 3i) - (5 + 5i) = \mathbf{-3 - 8i}$

11. $\overline{z}$

$1 - i$

12. $\overline{w}$

$2 + 3i$

13. $\overline{z} + \overline{w}$

$3 + 2i$

14. $\overline{z + w}$

$3 + 2i$

LEVEL 2

Find all square roots of each of the following complex numbers:

15. 4

We are looking for a complex number $a + bi$ such that $(a + bi)^2 = 4$. In other words, we need $(a + bi)(a + bi) = (a^2 - b^2) + 2abi$ to equal $4 = 4 + 0i$. So, we have $a^2 - b^2 = 4$ and $2ab = 0$. The second equation tells us that $a = 0$ or $b = 0$.

If $a = 0$, then $-b^2 = 4$, or equivalently, $b^2 = -4$. Since the square of a real number must be positive, this is impossible.

If $b = 0$, then $a^2 = 4$, and so, $a = \pm 2$.

It follows that the two square roots of 4 are **2** and **-2**.

16. $2i$

We are looking for a complex number $a + bi$ such that $(a + bi)^2 = 2i$. In other words, we need $(a + bi)(a + bi) = (a^2 - b^2) + 2abi$ to equal $2i = 0 + 2i$. So, we have $a^2 - b^2 = 0$ and $2ab = 2$, or equivalently, $ab = 1$. The first equation is equivalent to $(a + b)(a - b) = 0$, so that $a + b = 0$ or $a - b = 0$. It follows that $a = -b$ or $a = b$.

If $a = -b$, then $ab = (-b)b = -b^2$. So, $-b^2 = 1$, or equivalently, $b^2 = -1$. Since the square of a real number must be positive, this is impossible.

If $a = b$, then $ab = b^2$. So, $b^2 = 1$. Therefore, $b = \pm 1$. So, $a = \pm 1$.

It follows that the two square roots of i are **$1 + i$** and **$-1 - i$**.

Let $z = -4 - i$ and $w = 3 - 5i$. Compute each of the following:

17. zw

$zw = (-4 - i)(3 - 5i) = (-12 - 5) + (20 - 3)i = \mathbf{-17 + 17i}$.

18. $\frac{z}{w}$

$$\frac{z}{w} = \frac{-4-i}{3-5i} = \frac{(-4-i)(3+5i)}{(3-5i)(3+5i)} = \frac{(-12+5)+(-20-3)i}{3^2+5^2} = \frac{-7-23i}{9+25} = -\frac{7}{34} - \frac{23}{34}i.$$

19. $|z|$

$$|z| = \sqrt{(-4)^2 + (-1)^2} = \sqrt{16+1} = \sqrt{17}.$$

20. $|w|$

$$|w| = \sqrt{3^2 + (-5)^2} = \sqrt{9+25} = \sqrt{34}.$$

21. $|zw|$

$$|zw| = |-17+17i| = \sqrt{(-17)^2 + 17^2} = \sqrt{17^2 \cdot 2} = 17\sqrt{2}.$$

22. the distance between z and w.

$$|z-w| = |(-4-i)-(3-5i)| = |(-4-3)+(-1+5)i| = |-7+4i| = \sqrt{(-7)^2 + 4^2}$$
$$= \sqrt{49+16} = \sqrt{65}.$$

LEVEL 3

Determine if each of the following sets is open, closed, both, or neither.

23. $\emptyset$

Both

24. $\mathbb{C}$

Both

25. $\{z \in \mathbb{C} \mid |z| > 1\}$

Open

26. $\{z \in \mathbb{C} \mid \operatorname{Im} z \leq -2\}$

Closed

27. $\{i^n \mid n \in \mathbb{Z}^+\}$

Closed

28. $\{z \in \mathbb{C} \mid 2 < |z-2| < 4\}$

Open

A point w is an **accumulation point** of a set S of complex numbers if each deleted neighborhood of w contains at least one point in S. Determine the accumulation points of each of the following sets:

29. $\left\{\frac{1}{n} \,\middle|\, n \in \mathbb{Z}^+\right\}$

0 is the only accumulation point of this set.

30. $\left\{\frac{i}{n} \,\middle|\, n \in \mathbb{Z}^+\right\}$

0 is the only accumulation point of this set.

31. $\{i^n \mid n \in \mathbb{Z}^+\}$

This set is equal to $\{1, -1, i, -i\}$. It has **no accumulation points**.

32. $\left\{\frac{i^n}{n} \,\middle|\, n \in \mathbb{Z}^+\right\}$

0 is the only accumulation point of this set.

33. $\{z \mid |z| < 1\}$

The set of accumulation points of the set $\{z \mid |z| < 1\}$ is the set $\{\mathbf{z} \mid |\mathbf{z}| \le \mathbf{1}\}$.

34. $\{z \mid 0 < |z - 2| \le 3\}$

The set of accumulation points of the set $\{z \mid 0 < |z - 2| \le 3\}$ is the set $\{z \mid |z - 2| \le 3\}$.

35. $\{a + bi \mid a, b \in \mathbb{Z}\}$

The set of accumulation points of the set $\{a + bi \mid a, b \in \mathbb{Q}\}$ is $\emptyset$.

36. $\{a + bi \mid a, b \in \mathbb{Q}\}$

The set of accumulation points of the set $\{a + bi \mid a, b \in \mathbb{Q}\}$ is $\mathbb{C}$, the entire set of complex numbers.

LEVEL 4

Let z and w be complex numbers. Verify each of the following:

37. $\operatorname{Re} z = \frac{z + \bar{z}}{2}$

Let $z = a + bi$. Then $\bar{z} = a - bi$, and so, $\frac{z + \bar{z}}{2} = \frac{(a+bi) + (a-bi)}{2} = \frac{2a + bi - bi}{2} = \frac{2a}{2} = a = \operatorname{Re} z$.

38. $\operatorname{Im} z = \frac{z - \bar{z}}{2i}$

Let $z = a + bi$. Then $\frac{z-\bar{z}}{2i} = \frac{(a+bi)-(a-bi)}{2i} = \frac{a-a+bi+bi}{2i} = \frac{2bi}{2i} = b = \operatorname{Im} z$.

39. $\overline{z + w} = \bar{z} + \bar{w}$

Let $z = a + bi$ and $w = c + di$. Then we have

$$\overline{z + w} = \overline{(a + bi) + (c + di)} = \overline{(a + c) + (b + d)i} = (a + c) - (b + d)i$$
$$= (a - bi) + (c - di) = \overline{a + bi} + \overline{c + di} = \bar{z} + \bar{w}.$$

40. $\overline{zw} = \bar{z} \cdot \bar{w}$

Let $z = a + bi$ and $w = c + di$. Then we have

$$\overline{zw} = \overline{(a + bi)(c + di)} = \overline{(ac - bd) + (ad + bc)i} = (ac - bd) - (ad + bc)i$$
$$= (a - bi)(c - di) = \overline{(a + bi)}\,\overline{(c + di)} = \bar{z} \cdot \bar{w}.$$

41. $\overline{\left(\frac{z}{w}\right)} = \frac{\bar{z}}{\bar{w}}$

Let $z = a + bi$ and $w = c + di$. Then we have

$$\overline{\left(\frac{z}{w}\right)} = \overline{\frac{(a + bi)}{(c + di)}} = \overline{\frac{(a + bi)}{(c + di)} \cdot \frac{(c - di)}{(c - di)}} = \overline{\frac{(a + bi)(c - di)}{(c + di)(c - di)}} = \overline{\frac{(ac + bd) + (-ad + bc)i}{c^2 + d^2}}$$

$$= \overline{\frac{(ac + bd)}{c^2 + d^2} + \frac{(-ad + bc)}{c^2 + d^2}i} = \frac{(ac + bd)}{c^2 + d^2} - \frac{(-ad + bc)}{c^2 + d^2}i = \frac{(ac + bd) + (ad - bc)i}{c^2 + d^2}$$

$$= \frac{(a - bi)(c + di)}{(c - di)(c + di)} = \frac{(a - bi)}{(c - di)} \cdot \frac{(c + di)}{(c + di)} = \frac{a - bi}{c - di} = \frac{\overline{a + bi}}{\overline{c + di}} = \frac{\bar{z}}{\bar{w}}$$

42. $z\bar{z} = |z|^2$

Let $z = a + bi$. Then $z\bar{z} = (a + bi)(a - bi) = a^2 + b^2 = |z|^2$.

43. $|zw| = |z||w|$

$|zw|^2 = (zw)(\overline{zw}) = (zw)(\bar{z} \cdot \bar{w}) = z\bar{z}w\bar{w} = |z|^2|w|^2 = (|z||w|)^2$. Since $|z|$, $|w|$, and $|zw|$ are nonnegative, $|zw| = |z||w|$.

44. If $w \neq 0$, then $\left|\frac{z}{w}\right| = \frac{|z|}{|w|}$

Using Problem 43 above, we have $\left|\frac{z}{w}\right| = |zw^{-1}| = |z||w^{-1}| = \frac{|z|}{|w|}$.

45. $\operatorname{Re} z \leq |z|$

We have $|z|^2 = (\operatorname{Re} z)^2 + (\operatorname{Im} z)^2$. Therefore, $(\operatorname{Re} z)^2 \leq |z|^2$, and so, $|\operatorname{Re} z| \leq |z|$. It follows that $\operatorname{Re} z \leq |\operatorname{Re} z| \leq |z|$.

46. $\operatorname{Im} z \leq |z|$

We have $|z|^2 = (\operatorname{Re} z)^2 + (\operatorname{Im} z)^2$. Therefore, $(\operatorname{Im} z)^2 \leq |z|^2$, and so, $|\operatorname{Im} z| \leq |z|$. It follows that $\operatorname{Im} z \leq |\operatorname{Im} z| \leq |z|$.

47. $|z + w| \leq |z| + |w|$ (This is known as the **Triangle Inequality**.)

$$|z+w|^2 = (z+w)\overline{(z+w)} = (z+w)(\overline{z} + \overline{w}) = z\overline{z} + z\overline{w} + w\overline{z} + w\overline{w}$$

$$= z\overline{z} + z\overline{w} + \overline{z\overline{w}} + w\overline{w} = z\overline{z} + 2\operatorname{Re}(z\overline{w}) + w\overline{w} \leq z\overline{z} + 2|z\overline{w}| + w\overline{w} = z\overline{z} + 2|z||\overline{w}| + w\overline{w}$$

$$= |z|^2 + 2|z||w| + |w|^2 = (|z| + |w|)^2.$$

Since $|z + w|$ and $|z| + |w|$ are nonnegative, $|z + w| \leq |z| + |w|$.

Note: This result is known as the **Triangle Inequality**.

48. $\big||z| - |w|\big| \leq |z \pm w| \leq |z| + |w|.$

$|z| = |(z+w) + (-w)| \leq |z+w| + |-w| = |z+w| + |w|$. So, $|z+w| \geq |z| - |w|$.

$|w| = |(z+w) + (-z)| \leq |z+w| + |-z| = |z+w| + |z|$. So, $|z+w| \geq |w| - |z| = -(|z| - |w|)$.

Since for all $w, z \in \mathbb{C}$, we have $\big||z| - |w|\big| = |z| - |w|$ or $\big||z| - |w|\big| = -(|z| - |w|)$, it follows that $\big||z| - |w|\big| \leq |z + w|$.

Combining this result with the Triangle Inequality (Problem 47 above), gives us

$$\big||z| - |w|\big| \leq |z + w| \leq |z| + |w|.$$

Now, by the Triangle Inequality we have $|z - w| = |z + (-w)| \leq |z| + |-w| = |z| + |w|$.

Finally, by the third paragraph, we have $|z - w| = |z + (-w)| \geq \big||z| - |-w|\big| = \big||z| - |w|\big|$.

Let $c = 3 - i$ and $r = \sqrt{5}$. Use set-builder notation to describe each of the following:

49. The circle with center c and radius r.

$\{z \in \mathbb{C} \mid |z - (3 - i)| = \sqrt{5}\}$ or $\{x + yi \in \mathbb{C} \mid (x - 3)^2 + (y + 1)^2 = 5\}$

50. The open disk with center c and radius r.

$\{z \in \mathbb{C} \mid |z - (3 - i)| < \sqrt{5}\}$ or $\{x + yi \in \mathbb{C} \mid (x - 3)^2 + (y + 1)^2 < 5\}$

51. The closed disk with center c and radius r.

$\{z \in \mathbb{C} \mid |z - (3 - i)| \leq \sqrt{5}\}$ or $\{x + yi \in \mathbb{C} \mid (x - 3)^2 + (y + 1)^2 \leq 5\}$

52. The punctured open disk with center c and radius r.

$$\{z \in \mathbb{C} \mid 0 < |z - (3 - i)| < \sqrt{5}\} \text{ or } \{x + yi \in \mathbb{C} \mid 0 < (x - 3)^2 + (y + 1)^2 < 5\}$$

LEVEL 5

Verify each of the following:

53. An arbitrary union of open sets in $\mathbb{C}$ is an open set in $\mathbb{C}$.

Let X be a set of open subsets of $\mathbb{C}$ and let $z \in \bigcup X$. Then $z \in A$ for some $A \in X$. Since A is open in $\mathbb{C}$, there is an open disk D with $z \in D$ and $D \subseteq A$. By Problem 59 from Lesson 6, we have $A \subseteq \bigcup X$. Since $\subseteq$ is transitive, $D \subseteq \bigcup X$. Therefore, $\bigcup X$ is open.

54. An arbitrary intersection of closed sets in $\mathbb{C}$ is a closed set in $\mathbb{C}$.

Let X be a nonempty set of closed sets in $\mathbb{C}$. Then for each $A \in X$, $\mathbb{C} \setminus A$ is an open set in $\mathbb{C}$. By Problem 53 above, $\bigcup \{\mathbb{C} \setminus A \mid A \in X\}$ is open in $\mathbb{C}$. Therefore, $\mathbb{C} \setminus \bigcup \{\mathbb{C} \setminus A \mid A \in X\}$ is closed in $\mathbb{C}$. So, it suffices to show that $\bigcap X = \mathbb{C} \setminus \bigcup \{\mathbb{C} \setminus A \mid A \in X\}$. Well, $x \in \bigcap X$ if and only if for all $A \in X$, $x \in A$ if and only if for all $A \in X$, $x \notin \mathbb{C} \setminus A$ if and only if $x \notin \bigcup \{\mathbb{C} \setminus A \mid A \in X\}$ if and only if $x \in \mathbb{C} \setminus \bigcup \{\mathbb{C} \setminus A \mid A \in X\}$. So, $\bigcap X = \mathbb{C} \setminus \bigcup \{\mathbb{C} \setminus A \mid A \in X\}$, completing the argument.

A complex number z is an **interior point** of a set S of complex numbers if there is a neighborhood of z that contains only points in S, whereas w is a **boundary point** of S if each neighborhood of w contains at least one point in S and one point not in S. Show the following:

55. A set of complex numbers is open if and only if each point in S is an interior point of S.

Let S be a set of complex numbers. Then S is open if and only if for every complex number $z \in S$, there is an open disk D with $z \in D$ and $D \subseteq S$ if and only if for every complex number $z \in S$, there is a neighborhood of z that contains only points in S if and only if every complex number in S is an interior point of S.

56. A set of complex numbers is open if and only if it contains none of its boundary points.

Suppose that S is an open set of complex numbers and let $z \in S$. By Problem 55 above, z is an interior point of S. So, there is a neighborhood of z containing only points of S. So, z is **not** a boundary point of S. Since $z \in S$ was arbitrary, S contains none of its boundary points.

We now show that if S contains none of its boundary points, then S is open by contrapositive. Suppose S is not open. By Problem 55 above, there is $z \in S$ such that z is **not** an interior point. Let N be a neighborhood of z. Since $z \in S$, N contains a point in S (namely, z). Since z is not an interior point of S, N contains a point not in S. So, z is a boundary point of S. Therefore, S contains at least one of its boundary points.

57. A set of complex numbers is closed if and only if it contains all its boundary points.

First note that a complex number z is a boundary point of S if and only if z is a boundary point of $\mathbb{C} \setminus S$ (because $z \in S$ if and only if $z \notin \mathbb{C} \setminus S$, and vice versa).

Let S be a set of complex numbers. Then S is closed if and only if $\mathbb{C} \setminus S$ is open if and only if $\mathbb{C} \setminus S$ contains none of its boundary points (by Problem 56 above) if and only if $S = \mathbb{C} \setminus (\mathbb{C} \setminus S)$ contains all its boundary points.

LEVEL 1

Let $A = \begin{bmatrix} 1 & 6 & 3 & 4 \\ 2 & -1 & 8 & -3 \\ 5 & -6 & 7 & 20 \end{bmatrix}$. Determine each of the following, if it exists.

   1. a_{14}

$a_{14} = \mathbf{4}$

   2. a_{42}

a_{42} **does not exist** (the matrix does **not** have four rows)

   3. a_{31}

$a_{31} = \mathbf{5}$

   4. $a_{11} + a_{22} + a_{33}$

$a_{11} + a_{22} + a_{33} = 1 + (-1) + 7 = \mathbf{7}$

   5. $a_{12} - a_{21}$

$a_{12} - a_{21} = 6 - 2 = \mathbf{4}$

   6. $2A$

$2A = \begin{bmatrix} 2 & 12 & 6 & 8 \\ 4 & -2 & 16 & -6 \\ 10 & -12 & 14 & 40 \end{bmatrix}$

   7. $-3A$

$-3A = \begin{bmatrix} -3 & -18 & -9 & -12 \\ -6 & 3 & -24 & 9 \\ -15 & 18 & -21 & -60 \end{bmatrix}$

   8. What is the size of the matrix A?

$\mathbf{3 \times 4}$

Let $B = \begin{bmatrix} 0 & 2 & 0 \\ 1 & 15 & 1 \\ 8 & 7 & 5 \\ 6 & 9 & 3 \end{bmatrix}$. Determine each of the following, if it exists.

   9. b_{14}

b_{14} **does not exist** (the matrix does **not** have four columns)

    10. b_{42}

$b_{42} = \mathbf{9}$

    11. b_{31}

$b_{31} = \mathbf{8}$

    12. $b_{11} + b_{22} + b_{33}$

$b_{11} + b_{22} + b_{33} = 0 + 15 + 5 = \mathbf{20}$

    13. $b_{12} - b_{21}$

$b_{12} - b_{21} = 2 - 1 = \mathbf{1}$

    14. $4B$

$$4B = \begin{bmatrix} \mathbf{0} & \mathbf{8} & \mathbf{0} \\ \mathbf{4} & \mathbf{60} & \mathbf{4} \\ \mathbf{32} & \mathbf{28} & \mathbf{20} \\ \mathbf{24} & \mathbf{36} & \mathbf{12} \end{bmatrix}$$

    15. $-2B$

$$-2B = \begin{bmatrix} \mathbf{0} & \mathbf{-4} & \mathbf{0} \\ \mathbf{-2} & \mathbf{-30} & \mathbf{-2} \\ \mathbf{-16} & \mathbf{-14} & \mathbf{-10} \\ \mathbf{-12} & \mathbf{-18} & \mathbf{-6} \end{bmatrix}$$

    16. What is the size of the matrix B?

$\mathbf{4 \times 3}$

LEVEL 2

Compute each of the following, if possible:

    17. $\begin{bmatrix} 4 & 3 \\ 2 & 1 \end{bmatrix} + \begin{bmatrix} 1 & 2 \\ 3 & 4 \end{bmatrix}$

$\begin{bmatrix} \mathbf{5} & \mathbf{5} \\ \mathbf{5} & \mathbf{5} \end{bmatrix}$

    18. $\begin{bmatrix} 1 & 0 & -1 \\ 0 & 1 & 1 \end{bmatrix} + \begin{bmatrix} 1 & 0 & 2 \\ 0 & 1 & 3 \end{bmatrix}$

$\begin{bmatrix} \mathbf{2} & \mathbf{0} & \mathbf{1} \\ \mathbf{0} & \mathbf{2} & \mathbf{4} \end{bmatrix}$

19. $\begin{bmatrix} 1 & 0 & -1 \\ 0 & 1 & 1 \end{bmatrix} + \begin{bmatrix} 1 & 2 \\ 3 & 4 \end{bmatrix}$

Does not exist (the two matrices have different sizes)

20. $-2\begin{bmatrix} 4 & 3 \\ 2 & 1 \end{bmatrix} + 5\begin{bmatrix} 1 & 2 \\ 3 & 4 \end{bmatrix}$

$\begin{bmatrix} -3 & 4 \\ 11 & 18 \end{bmatrix}$

21. $\begin{bmatrix} 1 & 2 & 3 & 4 \\ 1 & -2 & 3 & -4 \\ 1 & -2 & 3 & 4 \end{bmatrix} + \begin{bmatrix} 2 & 3 & 5 & -3 \\ 2 & -1 & 8 & -1 \\ 5 & -2 & 7 & 3 \end{bmatrix}$

$\begin{bmatrix} 3 & 5 & 8 & 1 \\ 3 & -3 & 11 & -5 \\ 6 & -4 & 10 & 7 \end{bmatrix}$

22. $3\begin{bmatrix} 1 & 2 & 3 & 4 \\ 1 & -2 & 3 & -4 \\ 1 & -2 & 3 & 4 \end{bmatrix} + 4\begin{bmatrix} 2 & 3 & 5 & -3 \\ 2 & -1 & 8 & -1 \\ 5 & -2 & 7 & 3 \end{bmatrix}$

$\begin{bmatrix} 11 & 18 & 29 & 0 \\ 11 & -10 & 41 & -16 \\ 23 & -14 & 37 & 24 \end{bmatrix}$

23. $\begin{bmatrix} 1 \\ i \\ -i \\ -1 \end{bmatrix} + [1 \quad i \quad i \quad 1]$

Does not exist (the two matrices have different sizes)

24. $[i \quad i \quad i \quad i] + [1 + 2i \quad 1 + 3i \quad 1 + 4i \quad 1 + 5i]$

$[1 + 3i \quad 1 + 4i \quad 1 + 5i \quad 1 + 6i]$

25. $5[i \quad i \quad i \quad i] + 7[1 + 2i \quad 1 + 3i \quad 1 + 4i \quad 1 + 5i]$

$[7 + 19i \quad 7 + 26i \quad 7 + 33i \quad 7 + 40i]$

LEVEL 3

Compute each of the following, if possible:

26. $\begin{bmatrix} 2 & 0 & -3 \\ 0 & 1 & 4 \end{bmatrix} \cdot \begin{bmatrix} 1 & 1 & 3 & 0 \\ 1 & -4 & 2 & 0 \\ 2 & 0 & 1 & -4 \end{bmatrix}$

$$\begin{bmatrix} 2 & 0 & -3 \\ 0 & 1 & 4 \end{bmatrix} \cdot \begin{bmatrix} 1 & 1 & 3 & 0 \\ 1 & -4 & 2 & 0 \\ 2 & 0 & 1 & -4 \end{bmatrix} = \begin{bmatrix} -4 & 2 & 3 & 12 \\ 9 & -4 & 6 & -16 \end{bmatrix}$$

27. $\begin{bmatrix} 3 & -1 & 5 \end{bmatrix} \cdot \begin{bmatrix} -4 \\ -7 \\ 2 \end{bmatrix}$

$$\begin{bmatrix} 3 & -1 & 5 \end{bmatrix} \cdot \begin{bmatrix} -4 \\ -7 \\ 2 \end{bmatrix} = -12 + 7 + 10 = \mathbf{5}$$

28. $\begin{bmatrix} -4 \\ -7 \\ 2 \end{bmatrix} \cdot \begin{bmatrix} 3 & -1 & 5 \end{bmatrix}$

$$\begin{bmatrix} -4 \\ -7 \\ 2 \end{bmatrix} \cdot \begin{bmatrix} 3 & -1 & 5 \end{bmatrix} = \begin{bmatrix} -12 & 4 & -20 \\ -21 & 7 & -35 \\ 6 & -2 & 10 \end{bmatrix}$$

29. $\begin{bmatrix} a & b & c \\ d & e & f \\ g & h & i \end{bmatrix} \cdot \begin{bmatrix} 1 & 0 & 1 \\ 0 & 2 & 0 \\ 3 & 1 & 4 \end{bmatrix}$

$$\begin{bmatrix} a & b & c \\ d & e & f \\ g & h & i \end{bmatrix} \cdot \begin{bmatrix} 1 & 0 & 1 \\ 0 & 2 & 0 \\ 3 & 1 & 4 \end{bmatrix} = \begin{bmatrix} a+3c & 2b+c & a+4c \\ d+3f & 2e+f & d+4f \\ g+3i & 2h+i & g+4i \end{bmatrix}$$

30. $\begin{bmatrix} 1 & 0 & -1 \\ 0 & 1 & 1 \end{bmatrix} \cdot \begin{bmatrix} 1 & 0 & 2 \\ 0 & 1 & 3 \end{bmatrix}$

Does not exist (the number of rows of the second matrix is **not** equal to the number of columns of the first matrix)

Questions 31 through 44 require the following definition:

Let V be a vector space over a field $\mathbb{F}$ and let $U \subseteq V$. We say that U is a **subspace** of V if (i) $0 \in U$, (ii) for all $v, w \in U$, $v + w \in U$, and (iii) for all $v \in U$ and $k \in \mathbb{F}$, $kv \in U$.

Determine if each of the following subsets of $\mathbb{R}^2$ is a subspace of $\mathbb{R}^2$ (you may use Problem 59 below):

31. $A = \{(x, y) \mid x + y = 0\}$

Since $0 + 0 = 0$, $(0,0) \in A$.

Let $(x, y), (z, w) \in A$. Then $x + y = 0$ and $z + w = 0$. Therefore,

$$(x + z) + (y + w) = (x + y) + (z + w) = 0 + 0 = 0.$$

So, $(x, y) + (z, w) = (x + z, y + w) \in A$.

Let $(x, y) \in A$ and $k \in \mathbb{R}$. Then $x + y = 0$. So, $kx + ky = k(x + y) = k \cdot 0 = 0$ (by Problem 59).

So, $k(x, y) = (kx, ky) \in A$.

Therefore, A is a subspace of $\mathbb{R}^2$.

32. $B = \{(x, y) \mid xy = 0\}$

Since $0 \cdot 1 = 0$, we have $(0, 1) \in B$. Since $1 \cdot 0 = 0$, we have $(1, 0) \in B$. Adding these two vectors gives us $(1, 0) + (0, 1) = (1, 1)$. However, $1 \cdot 1 = 1 \neq 0$, and so, $(1, 1) \notin B$. So, B is not closed under addition. Therefore, B is **not** a subspace of $\mathbb{R}^2$.

33. $C = \{(x, y) \mid 2x = 3y\}$

Since $2 \cdot 0 = 0$ and $3 \cdot 0 = 0$, $2 \cdot 0 = 3 \cdot 0$. Therefore, $(0, 0) \in C$.

Let $(x, y), (z, w) \in C$. Then $2x = 3y$ and $2z = 3w$. Therefore,

$$2(x + z) = 2x + 2z = 3y + 3w = 3(y + w).$$

So, $(x, y) + (z, w) = (x + z, y + w) \in C$.

Let $(x, y) \in C$ and $k \in \mathbb{R}$. Then $2x = 3y$. So, $2(kx) = k(2x) = k(3y) = 3(ky)$.

So, $k(x, y) = (kx, ky) \in C$.

Therefore, A is a subspace of $\mathbb{R}^2$.

34. $D = \{(x, y) \mid x \in \mathbb{Q}\}$

Since $1 \in \mathbb{Q}$, $(1, 0) \in D$. Now, $\sqrt{2}(1, 0) = (\sqrt{2}, 0) \notin D$ because $\sqrt{2} \notin \mathbb{Q}$. So, D is not closed under scalar multiplication. Therefore, D is **not** a subspace of $\mathbb{R}^2$.

35. $E = \{(a, 0) \mid a \in \mathbb{R}\}$

Since $0 \in \mathbb{R}$, $(0, 0) \in E$.

If $(a, 0), (b, 0) \in E$ and $k \in \mathbb{R}$, then $(a, 0) + (b, 0) = (a + b, 0) \in E$ and $k(a, 0) = (ka, 0) \in E$.

Therefore, E is a subspace of V.

Let U be a subspace of a vector space V over the field $\mathbb{F}$. Explain why each of the following is true

36. Addition is associative in U.

Associativity is defined by a universal statement, and therefore, it is closed downwards (see the Note following Example 3.11).

37. Addition is commutative in U.

Commutativity is defined by a universal statement, and therefore, it is closed downwards (see the Note following Example 3.11).

38. Each element in U has an additive inverse in U (you may use Problem 60 below).

Let $x \in U$. Since $U \subseteq V$, $x \in V$. Therefore, there is $-x \in V$ such that $x + (-x) = (-x) + x = 0$. By property (iii) of a subspace, $-1x \in U$, and by Problem 60, $-1x = -x$. Since $x \in U$ was arbitrary, each element in U has an additive inverse in U.

39. $(U, +)$ is a commutative group.

This follows from Problems 36 through 38, together with properties (i) and (ii) of a subspace.

40. For each $x \in U$, $1x = x$.

If $x \in U$, then since $U \subseteq V$, $x \in V$. So, $1x = x$. Since $x \in U$ was arbitrary, for $x \in U$, $1x = x$.

41. For all $j, k \in \mathbb{F}$ and each $x \in U$, $(jk)x = j(kx)$.

This property is defined by a universal statement, and therefore, it is closed downwards (see the Note following Example 3.11).

42. For each $k \in \mathbb{F}$ and all $x, y \in U$, $k(x + y) = kx + ky$.

This property is defined by a universal statement, and therefore, it is closed downwards (see the Note following Example 3.11).

43. For all $j, k \in \mathbb{F}$ and each matrix $x \in U$, $(j + k)x = jx + kx$.

This property is defined by a universal statement, and therefore, it is closed downwards (see the Note following Example 3.11).

44. U is a vector space over $\mathbb{F}$.

This follows from Problems 39 through 44.

LEVEL 4

Let $\mathbb{F}$ be a field and let $\mathbb{F}^n = \{(a_1, a_2, \ldots, a_n) \mid a_i \in \mathbb{F} \text{ for each } i = 1, 2, \ldots, n\}$. Define addition and scalar multiplication on $\mathbb{F}^n$ as follows:

$$(a_1, a_2, \ldots, a_n) + (b_1, b_2, \ldots, b_n) = (a_1 + b_1, a_2 + b_2, \ldots, a_n + b_n).$$
$$k(a_1, a_2, \ldots, a_n) = (ka_1, ka_2, \ldots, ka_n).$$

Explain why each of the following is true

45. $\mathbb{F}^n$ is closed under addition.

Let $(a_1, a_2, ..., a_n), (b_1, b_2, ..., b_n) \in \mathbb{F}^n$. Then $a_1, a_2, ..., a_n, b_1, b_2, ..., b_n \in \mathbb{F}$. By definition, $(a_1, a_2, ..., a_n) + (b_1, b_2, ..., b_n) = (a_1 + b_1, a_2 + b_2, ..., a_n + b_n)$. Since $\mathbb{F}$ is closed under addition, $a_1 + b_1, a_2 + b_2, ..., a_n + b_n \in \mathbb{F}$. Therefore, $(a_1, a_2, ..., a_n) + (b_1, b_2, ..., b_n) \in \mathbb{F}^n$.

46. Addition is associative in $\mathbb{F}^n$.

Let $(a_1, a_2, ..., a_n), (b_1, b_2, ..., b_n), (c_1, c_2, ..., c_n) \in \mathbb{F}^n$. Since addition is associative in $\mathbb{F}$, we have

$$[(a_1, a_2, ..., a_n) + (b_1, b_2, ..., b_n)] + (c_1, c_2, ..., c_n) = (a_1 + b_1, a_2 + b_2, ..., a_n + b_n) + (c_1, c_2, ..., c_n)$$
$$= ((a_1 + b_1) + c_1, (a_2 + b_2) + c_2, ..., (a_n + b_n) + c_n)$$
$$= (a_1 + (b_1 + c_1), a_2 + (b_2 + c_2), ..., a_n + (b_n + c_n))$$
$$= (a_1, a_2, ..., a_n) + (b_1 + c_1, b_2 + c_2, ..., b_n + c_n)$$
$$= (a_1, a_2, ..., a_n) + [(b_1, b_2, ..., b_n) + (c_1, c_2, ..., c_n)].$$

47. Addition is commutative in $\mathbb{F}^n$.

Let $(a_1, a_2, ..., a_n), (b_1, b_2, ..., b_n) \in \mathbb{F}^n$. Since addition is commutative in $\mathbb{R}$, we have

$$(a_1, a_2, ..., a_n) + (b_1, b_2, ..., b_n) = (a_1 + b_1, a_2 + b_2, ..., a_n + b_n) = (b_1 + a_1, b_2 + a_2, ..., b_n + a_n)$$
$$= (b_1, b_2, ..., b_n) + (a_1, a_2, ..., a_n).$$

48. There is an identity $\mathbf{0}$ in $\mathbb{F}^n$.

We show that $(0, 0, ..., 0)$ is an additive identity for $\mathbb{F}^n$. Let $(a_1, a_2, ..., a_n) \in \mathbb{F}^n$. Since 0 is an additive identity for $\mathbb{R}$, we have

$$(0, 0, ..., 0) + (a_1, a_2, ..., a_n) = (0 + a_1, 0 + a_2, ..., 0 + a_n) = (a_1, a_2, ..., a_n).$$
$$(a_1, a_2, ..., a_n) + (0, 0, ..., 0) = (a_1 + 0, a_2 + 0, ..., a_n + 0) = (a_1, a_2, ..., a_n).$$

49. Each element in $\mathbb{F}^n$ has an additive inverse in $\mathbb{F}^n$.

Let $(a_1, a_2, ..., a_n) \in \mathbb{F}^n$. Then $a_1, a_2, ..., a_n \in \mathbb{F}$. Since $\mathbb{F}$ has the additive inverse property, $-a_1, -a_2, ..., -a_n \in \mathbb{F}$. So, $(-a_1, -a_2, ..., -a_n) \in \mathbb{F}^n$ and

$$(a_1, a_2, ..., a_n) + (-a_1, -a_2, ..., -a_n) = (a_1 - a_1, a_2 - a_2, ..., a_n - a_n) = (0, 0, ..., 0).$$
$$(-a_1, -a_2, ..., -a_n) + (a_1, a_2, ..., a_n) = (-a_1 + a_1, -a_2 + a_2, ..., -a_n + a_n) = (0, 0, ..., 0).$$

50. $(\mathbb{F}^n, +)$ is a commutative group.

This follows from Problems 45 through 49.

51. $\mathbb{F}^n$ is closed under scalar multiplication.

Let $k \in \mathbb{F}$ and let $(a_1, a_2, ..., a_n) \in \mathbb{F}^n$. Then $a_1, a_2, ..., a_n \in \mathbb{F}$. By definition, we have $k(a_1, a_2, ..., a_n) = (ka_1, ka_2, ..., ka_n)$. Since $\mathbb{F}$ is closed under multiplication, $ka_1, ka_2, ..., ka_n \in \mathbb{F}$. Therefore, $k(a_1, a_2, ..., a_n) \in \mathbb{F}^n$.

52. For each $x \in \mathbb{F}^n$, $1x = x$.

Let $(a_1, a_2, \dots, a_n) \in \mathbb{F}^n$. Then $1(a_1, a_2, \dots, a_n) = (1a_1, 1a_2, \dots, 1a_n) = (a_1, a_2, \dots, a_n)$.

53. For all $j, k \in \mathbb{F}$ and each $x \in \mathbb{F}^n$, $(jk)x = j(kx)$.

Let $j, k \in \mathbb{F}$ and $(a_1, a_2, \dots, a_n) \in \mathbb{F}^n$. Then since multiplication is associative in $\mathbb{F}$, we have
$$(jk)(a_1, a_2, \dots, a_n) = \big((jk)a_1, (jk)a_2, \dots, (jk)a_n\big) = (j(ka_1), j(ka_2), \dots, j(ka_n))$$
$$= j(ka_1, ka_2, \dots, ka_n) = j\big(k(a_1, a_2, \dots, a_n)\big).$$

54. For each $k \in \mathbb{F}$ and all $x, y \in \mathbb{F}^n$, $k(x + y) = kx + ky$.

Let $k \in \mathbb{F}$ and $(a_1, a_2, \dots, a_n), (b_1, b_2, \dots, b_n) \in \mathbb{F}^n$. Since multiplication is distributive over addition in $\mathbb{F}$, we have
$$k\big((a_1, a_2, \dots, a_n) + (b_1, b_2, \dots, b_n)\big) = k\big((a_1 + b_1, a_2 + b_2, \dots, a_n + b_n)\big)$$
$$= \big(k(a_1 + b_1), k(a_2 + b_2), \dots, k(a_n + b_n)\big) = \big((ka_1 + kb_1), (ka_2 + kb_2), \dots, (ka_n + kb_n)\big)$$
$$= (ka_1, ka_2, \dots, ka_n) + (kb_1, kb_2, \dots, kb_n) = k(a_1, a_2, \dots, a_n) + k(b_1, b_2, \dots, b_n).$$

55. For all $j, k \in \mathbb{F}$ and each matrix $x \in \mathbb{F}^n$, $(j + k)x = jx + kx$.

Let $j, k \in \mathbb{F}$ and $(a_1, a_2, \dots, a_n) \in \mathbb{F}^n$. Since multiplication is distributive over addition in $\mathbb{F}$, we have
$$(j + k)(a_1, a_2, \dots, a_n) = \big((j + k)a_1, (j + k)a_2, \dots, (j + k)a_n\big)$$
$$= (ja_1 + ka_1, ja_2 + ka_2, \dots, ja_n + ka_n) = (ja_1, ja_2, \dots, ja_n) + (ka_1, ka_2, \dots, ka_n)$$
$$= j(a_1, a_2, \dots, a_n) + k(a_1, a_2, \dots, a_n).$$

56. $\mathbb{F}^n$ is a vector space over $\mathbb{F}$.

This follows from Problems 50 through 55.

LEVEL 5

Let V be a vector space over a field $\mathbb{F}$. Explain why each of the following is true:

57. For every $v \in V$, $-(-v) = v$.

Since $-v$ is the additive inverse of v, we have $v + (-v) = -v + v = 0$. But this equation also says that v is the additive inverse of $-v$. So, $-(-v) = v$.

58. For every $v \in V$, $0v = 0$.

Let $v \in V$. Then $0v = (0 + 0)v = 0v + 0v$. So, we have
$$0 = -0v + 0v = -0v + (0v + 0v) = (-0v + 0v) + 0v = 0 + 0v = 0v.$$

59. For every $k \in \mathbb{F}$, $k \cdot 0 = 0$.

Let $k \in \mathbb{F}$. Then $k \cdot 0 = k(0 + 0) = k \cdot 0 + k \cdot 0$. So, we have

$$0 = -k \cdot 0 + k \cdot 0 = -k \cdot 0 + (k \cdot 0 + k \cdot 0) = (-k \cdot 0 + k \cdot 0) + k \cdot 0 = 0 + k \cdot 0 = k \cdot 0.$$

60. For every $v \in V$, $-1v = -v$.

Let $v \in V$. Then we have $v + (-1v) = 1v + (-1v) = \big(1 + (-1)\big)v = 0v = 0$ by Problem 58 and we have $-1v + v = -1v + 1v = (-1 + 1)v = 0v = 0$ again by Problem 58. So, $-1v = -v$.

Let $A = \begin{bmatrix} a & b \\ c & d \end{bmatrix}$ be a 2×2 matrix. We say that A is **invertible** if there is a 2×2 matrix B such that $AB = I$ and $BA = I$, where $I = \begin{bmatrix} 1 & 0 \\ 0 & 1 \end{bmatrix}$. Verify each of the following:

61. The inverse of $A = \begin{bmatrix} 1 & 1 \\ 0 & 1 \end{bmatrix}$ is $B = \begin{bmatrix} 1 & -1 \\ 0 & 1 \end{bmatrix}$.

$$\begin{bmatrix} 1 & 1 \\ 0 & 1 \end{bmatrix} \cdot \begin{bmatrix} 1 & -1 \\ 0 & 1 \end{bmatrix} = \begin{bmatrix} 1+0 & -1+1 \\ 0+0 & 0+1 \end{bmatrix} = \begin{bmatrix} 1 & 0 \\ 0 & 1 \end{bmatrix} = I$$

$$\begin{bmatrix} 1 & -1 \\ 0 & 1 \end{bmatrix} \cdot \begin{bmatrix} 1 & 1 \\ 0 & 1 \end{bmatrix} = \begin{bmatrix} 1+0 & 1+(-1) \\ 0+0 & 0+1 \end{bmatrix} = \begin{bmatrix} 1 & 0 \\ 0 & 1 \end{bmatrix} = I$$

Therefore, the inverse of A is B.

62. The zero matrix $\mathbf{0} = \begin{bmatrix} 0 & 0 \\ 0 & 0 \end{bmatrix}$ is **not** invertible.

For any 2×2 matrix $\begin{bmatrix} a & b \\ c & d \end{bmatrix}$, we have $\begin{bmatrix} 0 & 0 \\ 0 & 0 \end{bmatrix} \cdot \begin{bmatrix} a & b \\ c & d \end{bmatrix} = \begin{bmatrix} 0 & 0 \\ 0 & 0 \end{bmatrix} \neq \begin{bmatrix} 1 & 0 \\ 0 & 1 \end{bmatrix}$.

63. If $ad - bc \neq 0$, then $A = \begin{bmatrix} a & b \\ c & d \end{bmatrix}$ is invertible. In this case, what is the multiplicative inverse of A?

Let $B = \dfrac{1}{ad-bc} \begin{bmatrix} d & -b \\ -c & a \end{bmatrix}$. Then we have

$$AB = \begin{bmatrix} a & b \\ c & d \end{bmatrix} \cdot \frac{1}{ad-bc} \begin{bmatrix} d & -b \\ -c & a \end{bmatrix} = \frac{1}{ad-bc} \begin{bmatrix} ad-bc & a(-b)+ba \\ cd-dc & c(-b)+da \end{bmatrix}$$

$$= \frac{1}{ad-bc} \begin{bmatrix} ad-bc & 0 \\ 0 & ad-bc \end{bmatrix} = \begin{bmatrix} 1 & 0 \\ 0 & 1 \end{bmatrix} = I.$$

$$BA = \frac{1}{ad-bc} \begin{bmatrix} d & -b \\ -c & a \end{bmatrix} \cdot \begin{bmatrix} a & b \\ c & d \end{bmatrix} = \frac{1}{ad-bc} \begin{bmatrix} da-bc & db-bd \\ -ca+ac & -cb+ad \end{bmatrix}$$

$$= \frac{1}{ad-bc} \begin{bmatrix} ad-bc & 0 \\ 0 & ad-bc \end{bmatrix} = \begin{bmatrix} 1 & 0 \\ 0 & 1 \end{bmatrix} = I.$$

This shows that B is the multiplicative inverse of A.

About the Author

Dr. Steve Warner, a New York native, earned his Ph.D. at Rutgers University in Pure Mathematics in May 2001. While a graduate student, Dr. Warner won the TA Teaching Excellence Award.

After Rutgers, Dr. Warner joined the Penn State Mathematics Department as an Assistant Professor and in September 2002, he returned to New York to accept an Assistant Professor position at Hofstra University. By September 2007, Dr. Warner had received tenure and was promoted to Associate Professor. He has taught undergraduate and graduate courses in Precalculus, Calculus, Linear Algebra, Differential Equations, Mathematical Logic, Set Theory, and Abstract Algebra.

From 2003 – 2008, Dr. Warner participated in a five-year NSF grant, "The MSTP Project," to study and improve mathematics and science curriculum in poorly performing junior high schools. He also published several articles in scholarly journals, specifically on Mathematical Logic.

Dr. Warner has nearly two decades of experience in general math tutoring and tutoring for standardized tests such as the SAT, ACT, GRE, GMAT, and AP Calculus exams. He has tutored students both individually and in group settings.

In February 2010 Dr. Warner released his first SAT prep book "The 32 Most Effective SAT Math Strategies," and in 2012 founded Get 800 Test Prep. Since then Dr. Warner has written books for the SAT, ACT, SAT Math Subject Tests, AP Calculus exams, and GRE. In 2018 Dr. Warner released his first pure math book called "Pure Mathematics for Beginners." Since then he has released several more books, each one addressing a specific subject in pure mathematics.

Dr. Steve Warner can be reached at

steve@SATPrepGet800.com

BOOKS BY DR. STEVE WARNER

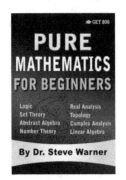   

  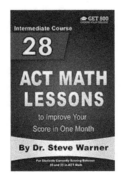 

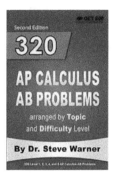
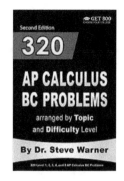

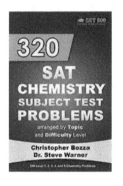
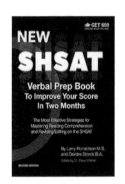

Printed in the USA
CPSIA information can be obtained
at www.ICGtesting.com
LVHW081546120924
790901LV00012B/498